Adult Safeguarding:
a care leader's guide

Supporting leaders in strategic and operational roles to safeguard adults who have no voice, through assertive leadership and focusing on the prevention of organisational abuse

Lynne Phair

First published in 2015

Hawker Publications, Culvert House, Culvert Road, London SW11 5DH
Tel: 020 7720 2108 Fax: 020 7498 3023
Website: www.careinfo.org

British Library Cataloguing in Publication Data
A catalogue record for this book is available from the British Library

ISBN 9781874 790648

Typesetting by Andrew Chapman
www.preparetopublish.com

Printed and bound in Great Britain by Berforts Information Press, Oxford

Author's biography
Lynne Phair JP, MA BSc Hons (Nursing) RMN RGN DPNS
Independent consultant nurse and expert witness
Lynne Phair Consulting Ltd

Lynne has always specialised in the care of older people, and has worked in the NHS, at the Department of Health as a clinical advisor and in the independent sector. She currently works as an independent consultant nurse and expert witness for older people and safeguarding vulnerable adults. She was a nursing expert on two public enquiries and was the lead health investigator into the neglect at Orchid View, West Sussex. She is also the clinical advisor for Milford Care, a Fellow of the University of Brighton and a visiting lecturer at the University of Worcester, She is a member of the editorial advisory boards of the *Journal of Dementia Care* and the *Journal of Adult Protection* and is a consultant to the Crisis Prevention Institute. She is also the author of the Sit & See™ tool. She has written widely, speaks nationally and has been an advisor to BBC Radio 4's *File on 4*, BBC *Panorama* and ITV's *Exposure*.

Contents

Foreword
Mervyn Eastman

Safeguarding policy and practice has, since the mid-80s, undergone numerous changes in labelling: old age abuse, elder abuse, protection of vulnerable adults and the like, reflecting how we as a society think about vulnerability, what constitutes harm and appropriate civic and civil responses to care.

More recently our attention in England has been focused on the implications of the Care Act (2014) which brought together the different legislative and guidance frameworks into a single unifying law. Sections 42-46 of the Care Act provides guidance, what it is and why it matters. Too frequently however there is a disconnect between policy intention and practice – a confusion, even ignorance, among professional practitioners and managers, let alone those holding governance positions at local level and certainly in the understanding and knowledge of the general public. It is one thing to be told that safeguarding duties apply to an adult who needs care and support, who is experiencing or is at risk of abuse or neglect, and who as a result of those needs is unable to protect themselves; it is quite another to provide coherent organisational systems and individual practice responses.

Public and third sector organisations with either a specific or general safeguarding responsibility produce guidance and commentary for a range of stakeholders engaged in safeguarding, to say nothing of the value and wealth of academic literature that is currently available. It is disturbing, however, that in spite of all this documentation in terms of guidance, policies, regulation standards and research into causes and effects, still far too many patients and residents in hospitals, nursing and care homes are brutalised and even killed by those employed or elected to care. Far too many experience negligence, treatment bordering on abuse and a total lack of compassion.

Lynne Phair has in this book attempted to reshape how we think about safeguarding, but more than that, or perhaps as a result, Lynne has provided a 'golden thread' throughout each chapter. A thread that she has pioneered over many years and a thread that needs at this time to be reinforced and strengthened more than ever at every level of our care commissioning, governance, management, provision and practice: *compassion*.

Sit & See™ is an observational tool Lynne has developed over the years that captures and records the smallest things that make the biggest difference. Its relevance to this book is evident. Each chapter is hallmarked throughout by what could be considered as 'small things', but in fact if a light is shone upon them they act as a beacon to educate, learn, reflect, and indeed change approaches to the whole safeguarding landscape, incorporating the very objectives behind the Care Act. Even the chapter titles act as prompts which, when read, will remind and inform readers that at the end of the day safeguarding is immensely personal. This is not the same as 'person-centred care'. What Lynne has achieved is to make safeguarding very personal to all those working in health and social care whether in governance, human resources, commissioning, social work, nursing, and clinical practice. Process and guidance and good practice are all important BUT must not drive our work and interventions. Instead kindness and compassion underpin our professional and organisational responses within the safeguarding framework, combined with passion and humanity. When Lynne speaks at conferences it is these emotions the delegates 'feel' and they are energised, moved, and challenged. In my view this is what Lynne has also demonstrated in this publication.

Mervyn Eastman
Co-founder and president
Practitioner Alliance for Safeguarding Adults (PASA UK)

Leadership is more than just good management, centrally it involves the ability to influence and inspire others across an organisation. Management is doing things right. Leadership is doing the right things
(Drucker 2009).

Positive care experiences are associated with senior staff leading by example, associated with a dispersed leadership approach that encourages and supports staff across an organisation to take responsibility.
(Lupton & Croft-White 2013)).

This book is dedicated to:
- those who have suffered neglect in places where they should have been safe. They include my dad and the residents who died, and those who survived, the abuse and neglect at Orchid View
- the families of people receiving abusive care who have been ignored or not believed
- care workers who have the courage to stand up and speak out for adults who have no voice.

Introduction

I have decided to write this book because I want others to have the opportunity to think about how leaders of care services can ensure the people who use their services are not harmed, mistreated, neglected or abused. Prevention is always better than cure, and I believe that there are numerous strategies and systems that can be implemented to reduce the risk of abuse and neglect. I have worked as a nurse since 1977. The term abuse only became part of the vocabulary in the 1980s when it was sometimes referred to as 'granny bashing'. Organisational abuse was a new concept. Large organisations such as long-stay wards in mental hospitals cared for people in a highly structured way. General hospital wards were also run in a very formalised fashion with strict routines and rituals performed by the nurses. Evidence-based practice and individualised care as concepts were not known at this time.

Care was delivered with the best of intentions but, reflecting back now, some of it could have been considered as abusive care. This 'care' could have included activities such as teaching student nurses such as myself how to restrain a person in a tip-back chair, or how to tie a person's hands to the bed rails to stop them pulling out their tubes or intravenous lines. Far too many older people were routinely catheterised when admitted into a general hospital. During my mental health training in 1981 I was taught how to do 'bundles', which would involve going into a storeroom and selecting a set of clothes that I decided a patient should wear the next day. Dressing patients in clothes which were not their own and using stock underwear was common. Doors were routinely locked to prevent patients from having the opportunity to enter or leave the ward, regardless of whether there were any risks associated with their mental health condition. All patients who were capable had to attend the occupational or industrial therapy departments between 10 and 12 in the morning and between 2 and 4 in the afternoon.

Care workers rarely challenged these routine and ritualistic practices as they were there to care and to carry out task-focused work. Such organisational practices did not mean that patients were treated in an uncaring way. However, the systems ran the risk of treating patients without individual consideration thus eroding their individual dignity. Today such treatment would be considered evidence of organisational abuse.

I have always tried, sometimes naively, to stand up for what I believed intuitively was right for patients, Sometimes this meant I behaved insensitively to other staff, but it was always with the intention of improving the care and wellbeing of frail or older people. I have had many experiences of doing the right thing the right way for everyone, but also doing the right thing for patients which was perceived by staff as being the wrong way for them. Sometimes I have unconsciously known that something needed to change and achieved this with the full support and understanding of staff. On other occasions, however, I have achieved the right outcome for patients but this has had sad consequences for colleagues or others who felt threatened by change.

A career of 37 years cannot be anything but littered with challenging stories about the changes in personal, professional and societal attitudes towards care. These changes have resulted, over time, in some previously acceptable approaches to care now being considered, quite rightly, as abusive. As care practices change and develop, the biggest lesson I believe we can learn is to reflect honestly on what we did as professionals in the past in the light of the wisdom and improved practices and understanding we have now. As a professional and a human being, did I deliver the care in the past based, at that time, on current known best practice? Or did I deliver care knowing that I was inappropriately using my power and position or cutting corners?

Equally, I sometimes wonder whether I failed the patients by not taking matters further when I reflect on care that I felt was abusive, even in the 1980s, and reported it, but was not believed and told I was a trouble maker. Reflecting on another era does not make the abuse any more acceptable, but the culture of care together with societal and professional expectations of the era need to be considered as part of how we develop and improve our understanding of abuse and how to prevent it occurring. The harmful care of the past must never be justified, but understanding the context and societal norms will assist in the process of personal development and reconciliation.

Today health and social care is supported by international evidence-based practice. The internet enables easy access to knowledge for everyone and a plethora of organisations support the development and implementation of current practice. The individual rights of all adults are recognised and enshrined in law in various ways across the United Kingdom and the abuse of vulnerable adults or adults at risk of harm is recognised. The need to prevent mistreatment and abuse is also supported across society and the media. The need to improve expectations, however, continues because so often the low expectations of older people, their families and society breed complacency and an acceptance of low and unacceptable standards of care.

A significant contribution to the research into abuse of vulnerable adults in the UK has been undertaken by a collaboration of universities and research organisations brought together by funding provided by the Department of Health (England) and Comic Relief. Comic Relief has been supporting work to promote the rights, and meet the needs, of older people since 1990. The project had two phases. The first was the *UK Study of Abuse and Neglect of Older People* published in 2007. The second phase, started in 2008, included a series of 11 separate but linked research studies exploring a variety of aspects and issues that impact on safeguarding in hospitals and care homes and became known as the PANICOA (Prevention of Abuse and Neglect in the Organisational Care of Older Adults) initiative. The research set out to improve our understanding of the context, causes and consequences of mistreatment in organisational settings. Each project had an independent report and a full PANICOA report was also prepared. The overarching report *Respect and Protect* looks at the findings and combines them to identify common themes and issues. These are drawn together to form narratives and a template for good practice designed to reinforce or improve current practice in respect of both the care service and care culture of provider organisations.

The inquest into the deaths of 19 people at the Orchid View care home in West Sussex in 2011 made national headlines. The multi-agency investigation, and subsequent serious case review, brought into the public arena the catastrophic impact on residents of neglectful practices and incompetent and weak management and leadership at all levels of an organisation. The *Serious Case Review* (Georgiou 2014) made 34 recommendations, many of them applying to both the health and social care sectors. Everyone can learn from the suffering of the residents at Orchid View and, in my view, all leaders have a duty to do so.

This small book is my contribution to supporting positive leadership. It draws on my nursing knowledge, skills and experience of caring for older people, and also on my role as a consultant nurse investigating allegations of neglect over many years. It offers tips and ideas at a practical level as well as advice on how to put into practice the PANICOA recommendations and those of the *Orchid View Serious Case Review*.

This book is for leaders, not simply managers. I want leaders to think about and develop new skills and approaches to their role, hopefully avoiding some of the pitfalls of focusing only on the organisation, on the staff, budgets, audits or corporate issues, and failing to hold the resident central to all their activity.

The ten chapters set out the legislative framework and offer ideas, views, tips and pointers to prevent mistreatment or organisational abuse or neglect insidiously developing in a care setting. The tips and suggestions are presented in a format which reinforces my conviction that good anticipatory procedures and practices can reduce the risk of neglect and abuse, as well as preventing abusive cultures of care developing. The ideas are offered, at the end of each chapter, for primary, secondary and tertiary prevention using the Smallbone Resilience Model which is described in more detail in Chapter 1.

I believe that, as leaders, we must continuously examine ourselves and how we lead staff and uphold standards which enable older people and their families to live their lives in the manner they wish. All leaders, all the time, must understand the potential in all of us to lead a neglectful service or condone abusive systems if we don't have courage and pride in the work we do.

Our personal commitment and self-belief around safeguarding adults requires us to examine ourselves and our own practice before we can then consider the behaviour and actions of others. Despite public, political, and organisational claims that we must all stand up and be counted, and that whistleblowing and fighting for those who have no voice is the right thing to do, the impact these actions can have at personal and professional levels must never be underestimated. Challenging organisational abuse and neglect is essential but it requires great courage; a courage that can be career limiting, personally painful and, sometimes, psychologically damaging.

This book is my contribution to supporting those care leaders in health and social care who, disregarding those who may try to influence them otherwise, have the courage to stand up for those who have no voice and who want to support everyone within their teams to do the same.

Chapter 1:
Reshaping how we consider safeguarding

What is adult safeguarding in health and social care today?

The protection of adults who may be at risk of abuse has had many names since it was first voiced as an issue by professionals such as Mervyn Eastman in the 1970s and 1980s. The description has changed as understanding has improved. The term 'adult protection' is now considered inappropriate as it suggests a paternalistic approach from organisations which, having investigated abuse, prevent those responsible from harming the person again and so 'protect' the adult, regardless of their wishes and what they want the outcome to be. Safeguarding 'adults at risk' is the most recent commonly used phrase. However, following the example of the new Care Act in England, in this book the single word 'adults' will be used.

The phrase 'safeguarding' has been introduced to try and promote an approach that is focused on the prevention of abuse and it is now used routinely instead of adult protection. However, generally, the meaning and focus remain the same. It is not uncommon to hear that a person has 'raised a safeguarding', meaning that a concern has been identified and reported to the local authority.

A model of safeguarding

Training, education and activity for safeguarding should use a model that will support prevention, empowerment and protection, while ensuring the resident or patient remains central to all activities. My model includes:

1. prevention
2. learning from others
3. investigation
4. practice and policy development.

Examples and ideas of how to populate these four aspects of the model will be covered through the book.

Types of abuse

It is important at the beginning of a book on safeguarding to remind ourselves of what abuse looks like in the context of adults, and the types of abuse that can be seen in organisational settings. Types of abuse have been well-documented and traditionally include:

- neglect
- organisational abuse
- physical abuse
- psychological abuse
- sexual abuse
- financial abuse.

More recently, new types of abuse which have come under the umbrella of safeguarding (but not relevant to this book) include:

- criminal activity such as human trafficking
- honour-based crime
- honour-based killing
- domestic abuse.

Some of these further types of abuse may be easier to understand than others, but all deserve detailed attention which cannot be given here.

The focus of this book is on why and how our leaders in care homes should become more aware of the risks of abuse generally, principally by becoming more mindful of the possibilities and aware of the potential of 'man's inhumanity to man'. Leaders will be taught to have heightened awareness so they can identify subtle signs of distress or unexplained activity and be able to act accordingly. This could vary from undertaking a routine critical analysis of incident reports to noticing and hearing hesitation in a young carer's voice when she says she has to go abroad to be married to a man she has never met.

The most important attributes a leader can have are an open mind, wide eyes, a healthy suspicion, and a willingness to listen and hear what is being said or not said. This book will focus on how to prevent the most common types of abuse in care settings. To prevent these, first it is vital to understand them.

Poor care, neglect – or 'just one of those things'?

It is not unusual to hear the term 'neglect' being used interchangeably with poor care, suboptimal care or shortcomings in care. The reasons are generally threefold:

1. Specific organisations have a definition that they are obliged to work to which is not appropriate to the given situation. For example, the coroner service in England and Wales can only give a conclusion that a death is caused by neglect when there has been a gross failure to provide adequate nourishment or liquids, or provide or procure basic medical attention to someone in a dependent position.
2. The organisation is concerned about using the word neglect as they fear civil action will be taken for negligence or they do not want to use the word neglect as it is uncomfortable for them.
3. The people describing neglect cannot bring themselves to use the word as they do not want to face the reality of the harm caused, or they do not understand that neglect does not have to be intentional to have occurred.

Neglect is defined in The Care Act 2014 as acts of omission which include:

• ignoring medical or physical care needs
• the failure to provide access to appropriate health, social care or educational services
• the withholding of the necessities of life such as medication, adequate nutrition and heating.

The National Midwifery Council uses this definition: "Neglect is the refusal or failure on the part of the registrant to meet the essential care needs of a client, for example, failure to attend to personal hygiene." (www.nmc-uk.org)'

Neither of the above definitions indicates that malicious intent is required to be proved for neglect to have occurred. The difference between poor care and neglect can be difficult to determine and the decision as to whether a person has been neglected usually requires skilled review of the evidence by an appropriate professional.

A frail, older person with advanced dementia, for example, may not be able to eat or drink without encouragement, may not be able to reposition themselves or sit up unaided. They may not have any awareness of hot and cold, be able to describe pain, or ask for help in any aspect of their activities of daily living. Due to their age and frailty, and the ageing process, it may be normal for them to be at high risk of urinary or chest infections, be stiff and unable to move about and to lose weight due to the dementia. If such a person is admitted to hospital from a care home with pneumonia, dehydration and pressure sores, it is understand-able and appropriate that a safeguarding concern is raised. The alert has identified that the condition of the person is 'unexplained'. It should not indicate that the person has been neglected. An enquiry into the facts should examine not only the condition of the person, but how that condition developed. Neglect will be proven if there is evidence that the person was not assessed and supported using current care practice to eat, drink, sit up, move about and have good skin hygiene.

If all of these things were done, it could be concluded that the person was not neglected, but the dehydration and pressure ulcers were a sad consequence of their condition. If, however, care plans were not written and appropriate preventative action not taken, neglect could be concluded. Lack of documentation alone does not constitute neglect, but could indicate poor care. The differential factor is the consequence of the lack of written care planning.

If a frail, older person is at high risk of falling, a full risk assessment will describe the actions to be taken to reduce the risk of harm from the fall. If the risk assessment has been done, correct control measures put in place and the care setting has tried everything it could to prevent harm, and the person still falls, then the care setting could not be held accountable or found guilty of neglect or poor care. However, if the person had no risk assessment, or a poorly completed one, and then fell, the outcome would be neglect as the lack of care documentation and assessment added and contributed to the harm caused. Conversely, if the person had no risk assessment, but did not fall and so suffered no harm, this would be due to poor care; that is, poor documentation.

The definition of poor care can also vary. What is poor care for one person could be neglect for another. Failure to give a drink to a fit, young person would not have the same impact as failing to give a drink to a frail, older person who perhaps has dementia, where the consequence of reduced fluids could be catastrophic and the impact of the poor care becomes evident very much more quickly.

Thus, all situations should be examined on a case-by-case basis and the term 'neglect' cannot be decided simply on the initial presentation of a person. Neglect is determined by examining the journey the person took to arrive in that condition. The determinants of neglect used by the DH (Phair and Heath 2009) offer further guidance on how to make judgements in difficult cases.

Organisational abuse

Organisational abuse (previously referred to as institutional abuse) occurs when the routine systems and regimes of an organisation result in poor or inadequate standards of care, or poor practice. It can also take the form of an organisation failing to respond to, or address, poor practice which has been brought to their attention (www.scie.org.uk).

This type of abuse often means the systems, rituals and routines that form the focus of activity for residents are centred on the needs of the staff or the organisation rather than those of the residents. It has to be said, though, that as in any organisation, there will be administrative compromises in a care home, because it is impossible to offer every resident a totally person-centred care package when others are sharing the same service. It would not be possible, for example, to help everyone to go to bed at exactly the same time if everyone had a preference for that time.

The question as to whether the routines and rituals of a particular home constitute organisational abuse is determined by the overall impact they have on the person. All organisations need some routines, systems, policies and procedures and the key question is the extent to which they benefit the residents. There are some activities, for example, that a person might be able to do in their own home, but cannot do in the organisational setting because of laws that affect community settings or because of the sheer numbers of people who live in the same environment.

A leader needs to be constantly mindful about whether the demands of the organisation have a negative impact on the occupants. They also need to be vigilant that custom and practices do not develop 'a life of their own' and become labelled as 'policy' by the staff. This can easily occur when ritualistic practices are passed on from one staff member to another, explanations for the practices are not given or reasons are not explored and they become set in stone. If the team leader is not alert to the real reasons for the practices and procedures of the care setting and if they do not remain reflective about why everything is done, organisational abuse could develop.

EXAMPLES

- Night nurses in a care home routinely did the medicine rounds at 6.30am instead of 8am as stated on the medicine administration chart. This was because there were a lot of medicines to administer and the night shift ended at 8am and the day staff said it was not their job. Residents suffered, however, because medication was not given in accordance with the prescription and the effects and benefits of the medicines were compromised.

- A care home allocated staff to different units each morning, regardless of where they had been on duty the day before or whether they knew the residents, so the staff did not get bored or frustrated with care for the same residents with dementia. The impact on the residents, however, was increased agitation and distress as staff were not able to make a relationship with residents and learn how they communicated. The more a care setting is ritual and procedure driven, the easier it becomes for it to become abusive.

Physical and psychological abuse

It could be argued that physical and psychological abuse are obvious and do not require definition. However, both can be subtle and not as obvious as the hitting, shouting or kicking a person as evidenced in the criminal assaults witnessed on residents at Winterbourne View. For example, physical abuse may include the use of restraint. This may be the inappropriate use of bed rails, taking away a buzzer or putting heavy furniture in front of a person who is sitting in a chair.

Physical abuse may be suspected if a person suffers from 'unexplained' bruising. There are many reasons for bruising, and so the person's medical history, medication, age and skin condition and level of independence or propensity to fall should be considered alongside the explanation by the staff member(s) of the circumstances in which the bruising took place. The use of body mapping and photography will assist in evaluating and monitoring any reasons for concern.

Psychological abuse can be subtle and difficult for the team leader to observe, especially if it occurs when staff are working in the resident's own room. It is often seen as a form of bullying where the workers use their position to assert power and control over the resident. Psychological abuse undermines the victim, commonly causing anxiety, distress and depression. In the *Panorama* programme 'Behind Closed Doors' (BBC 2014) a resident, Joan, was taunted and verbally abused by a senior care assistant. She was goaded and encouraged to react while the senior care assistant escalated the situation, laughing and appearing to enjoy the activity. In the same programme, Yvonne was psychologically abused by staff who failed to respond to her calls for help to go to the toilet for over two hours. When some staff did eventually attend, she was told to defecate in the pad, an action that was demoralising, degrading and distressing for her.

Sexual abuse

Sexual abuse is often difficult to understand, detect and manage. Sexual abuse can include rape, indecent assault and inappropriate touching. It may also include inappropriate sexual conversation, innuendo or joking. In some resident/carer relationships, the boundary between what could be considered appropriate adult-to-adult, respectful, positive, light-hearted chat, and what is insensitive sexual abuse, can be difficult to determine. Much will depend on the context, content, location, cultural norms and cultural background of the resident.

It should be added that male carers can feel very vulnerable themselves if they are carrying out personal care of any type for female residents.

Financial abuse

When care settings are supporting residents to manage their finances, staff may be exposed to the person's bank and other financial details and have opportunities to abuse that trust. Sadly there are plenty of examples of care staff stealing from residents. Staff are in a unique position of trust, thus any financial impropriety is abuse and should be regarded as theft and reported to the police. It would be unfortunate, however, and very sad if care staff were prevented from being able to support residents to go to the shops because of the risk that there are unscrupulous people who may take advantage of the relationship.

The difficulty with cases of financial abuse is finding the evidence and achieving successful prosecutions. Issues arise such as: has the resident the mental capacity to make financial decisions, such as willingly giving money or property to the care staff?

For the care home, clear policies, procedures and checking systems are required as well as a culture in which all staff know the risks of handling money or accepting gifts from residents, and therefore act appropriately. The team leader should:

- always insist on knowing about any financial transactions involving staff and residents
- always be mindful that a third party may be receiving financial details from staff in the care setting and using them to access a resident's bank accounts
- support the culture of care in which everyone working in the care setting is empowered and confident enough to play their part in safeguarding residents and patients.

EXAMPLE

A care assistant had worked for eight years with residents in the care home. She was fastidious and hardworking, and all criminal record checks were up to date and demonstrated that there was no history of criminal activity. She was a key worker for a lady who liked to go to the supermarket to shop. The resident was in a wheelchair and could not reach the counter, and so asked the care assistant to enter her PIN number into the card reader to pay for her purchases. A few weeks later, the lady became very distressed as she found she had no money in her bank account. An investigation revealed that the care assistant had intercepted a new bank card and had withdrawn £40,000 from her account. The care assistant was found guilty and sentenced to one year in prison.

Resilience-building model

Safeguarding needs to be proactive and preventative and the safeguarding model adopted by an organisation should support these ideals. It is important that safeguarding children and safeguarding adults are not compared or considered the same, as the two areas of safeguarding have different causes, approaches and legal frameworks.

That said, it may be beneficial for those concerned with adult safeguarding to consider an approach put forward by Stephen Smallbone (2008) and used by the Lucy Faithfull Foundation in preventing child sexual abuse. Smallbone describes how the traditional approach to child sexual abuse relies heavily on formal general deterrence strategies, relying on the assumption that widespread publicity about successful prosecutions would deter potential sex offenders from committing such offences themselves.

In adult safeguarding this would equate to assuming that all staff in health and social care settings would read reports such as the Mid Staffordshire Public Enquiry report or the *Orchid View Serious Case Review* and then, using the information they have gained from the reports, identify the risks in their own care settings to reduce the risks of abuse occurring there.

The problem is that experience suggests this traditional deterrence model, such as posters telling people to report abuse and having whistleblowing reporting call centres, does not work. This is evidenced by the number of enquiries, investigations and reports that have been conducted in the UK over the past 20 years which have had little or no impact on eliminating abuse. Examples of reports include *Hungry to be Heard* (Age Concern 2006), the Rowan Ward Inquiry (CHI 2003) and the Gosport Memorial Hospital review (Baker 2003).

Smallbone suggests an alternative approach may be to shift the focus from the traditional 'resistance training model', which in child sexual abuse involves teaching children to stay safe, to the 'resilience-building model'. This model involves looking at prevention at a primary, secondary and tertiary level and could be applied and adapted to adult safeguarding:

- **Primary prevention** refers to raising general awareness in the community and could include general, good safeguarding activity, policy and procedures. It could also include general procedures and information for families and residents.
- **Secondary prevention** refers to specific activity taken to prevent abuse. This could include staff supervision, role modelling positive practices, auditing and reviewing care practice and how successful in practice the focus on the culture of care is. This model would actively consider relatives and residents, residents' feedback meetings, and all aspects of resident and relative engagement.
- **Tertiary prevention** refers to how a leader responds to, manages and undertakes an enquiry after an incident has occurred, or at the point of a concern being identified. Success depends on keeping families, relatives and residents well informed, undertaking appropriate levels of review of information and enquiry, fully participating in safeguarding activity and holding staff to account.

How can we learn ?

The *Orchid View Serious Case Review* (Georgiou 2014) highlighted the fact that safeguarding concerns were raised repeatedly over 18 months and yet ignored. For example, one of the concerns that was repeatedly raised was medication administration. Yet there was no evidence that the nurses, managers or senior managers of the organisation used the evidence that was coming forward to learn, reflect and improve medication management.

By contrast, findings in the Choice project (Killett, Bowes *et al* 2013) showed that having a shared purpose, having a sense of community, and ensuring staff were empowered to take responsibility for residents' wellbeing using active management processes all have a bearing on the quality of care. Understanding and acting on these factors, whatever the circumstances, is the first step to promoting a safe and positive culture of care for residents.

Throughout this book, at the end of each chapter, ideas and suggestions will be given on how to actively safeguard residents in a care home setting by using Smallbone's model of suggestions for primary, secondary, and tertiary prevention.

POINTERS FOR PREVENTION OF ABUSE

1 Primary prevention
General activities, for example...

Put posters on staff information boards highlighting the different types of abuse.

2 Secondary prevention
Specific activities, for example...

Ensure the safeguarding training includes self-awareness, and covers organisational abuse.

3 Tertiary prevention
A response to an actual situation, for example...

If there has been a report about abuse in the media, obtain some more detailed information and discuss the case with staff. Focus on how to prevent the same situation in your home.

Chapter 2
The legal framework of adult safeguarding

The chapters in this book are set out to give practical and reflective support in respect of building and upholding a positive culture of care, wherever the care home is located. This work can be done within an overall framework of the safeguarding legislation, as it is based on practice and holding the resident central to the philosophy of the home and the care leader. It is important however, for the care leader to understand the legislation in which good practice in adult safeguarding sits.

There is a plethora of legislation that is designed to protect adults from harm or uphold the rights of individuals. Examples include health and safety laws, equal opportunity and anti-discrimination legislation, the Safeguarding Vulnerable Groups Act, Mental Capacity Act and Adults with Incapacity (Scotland) Act to list but a few.

Legislation to support and protect adults at risk of abuse and harm has been slow to materialise across the UK. Scotland was the first nation to have legislation in 2007. Since then the other three countries have either developed or are in the process of developing their own legislative framework.

A book cannot give a constantly up-to-the-minute description of legislation or statutory guidance in an evolving world such as adult safeguarding. However, it can give an overview of the legislation at the time of publication (2015), and can give the reader the incentive to continue to follow developments or adjustments to legislation over the years that follow.

The legal framework for adult safeguarding in England

In England, new legislation, the Care Act 2014, modernises and consolidates the law on adult care into one statute and has been described as the biggest change to the law in 60 years.

Key changes included in the Care Act 2014 include:

- the introduction of national eligibility criteria
- a right to independent advocacy
- rights for informal carers
- a cap on care costs faced by people who fund their own care.

The statutory guidance for Adult Safeguarding is contained in Chapter 14 of the guidance for the Act (Department of Health 2014). This replaces the Department of Health Guidance 'No Secrets' (2000).

The statutory guidance makes it quite clear that safeguarding is not a substitute for:

- providers' responsibilities to provide safe and high quality care and support
- commissioners regularly assuring themselves of the safety and effectiveness of commissioned services
- the Care Quality Commission (CQC) ensuring that regulated providers comply with the fundamental standards of care or taking enforcement action
- the core duties of the police to prevent and detect crime and protect life and property.

The Act puts a legal duty on local authorities that they **must**:

- make enquiries, or cause others to do so, if they believe an adult with care and support needs is subject to, or at risk of, abuse or neglect and, due to their care and support needs, is unable to protect themselves. An enquiry should enable the local authority to establish whether any action needs to be taken to stop or prevent abuse or neglect, and if so by whom (Section 42)
- set up a Safeguarding Adults Board (SAB) with core membership from the local authority, the police and the local Clinical Commissioning Group(s) (CCGs) of the NHS with the power to include anyone they think can assist them in their work, for example individuals or representatives of organisations who work with adults who may be at risk of harm.
- co-operate with each of its relevant partners in order to protect adults experiencing or at risk of abuse or neglect.

The duties of the Safeguarding Adults Board

Each local authority *must* set up a Safeguarding Adults Board (SAB), the main objective of which is to assure itself that local safeguarding arrangements and partners act to help and protect adults in its area who meet the criteria for safeguarding.

There are three core duties for the SAB:

1. it must publish a strategic plan for each financial year
2. it must publish an annual report
3. it must conduct any Safeguarding Adults Review in accordance with Section 44 of the Act.

Additionally, safeguarding requires collaboration between partners in order to create a framework of inter-agency arrangements which will become the local policy and procedures.

The SAB can decide its own structure and governance processes, including setting up sub-groups, which could be task and finish groups focusing on specific issues or long-standing committees monitoring and advising the SAB on issues such as quality, prevention activity or safeguarding training and education.

The scope or criteria for inclusion in adult safeguarding processes

There is no definition of who may be viewed as at risk of abuse or neglect, rather a 'scope or criteria' for who is included in adult safeguarding. Thus adult safeguarding will include anyone where the local authority has reasonable cause to suspect that an adult in its area (whether or not ordinarily resident there):

- has needs for care and support (whether or not the authority is meeting any of those needs)
- is experiencing, or is at risk of, abuse or neglect and
- as a result of those needs is unable to protect himself or herself against the abuse or neglect or the risk of it.

There is an expectation that some concerns previously dealt with by some local authorities under safeguarding will now be reviewed by other processes and procedures, such as quality assurance or commissioning procedures, or by the Care Quality Commission. Alternatively other concerns, traditionally raised as safeguarding in one sector but not in another (for example the development of a pressure ulcer), might now be recorded using the internal organisation reporting system and investigated as a clinical /care incident. The type of concern and how these departments will work together to ensure consistency and proportionality will be decided locally by the SAB and details will be set out in the local policy. Thus some concerns that used to be considered as a safeguarding matter will not now be managed or reviewed under the safeguarding system. The deciding factor which local authorities should consider when determining the best approach to reviewing a concern is by reference to the criteria.

The language of adult safeguarding

There is a new language for safeguarding in the Care Act. Some of this is already used in some localities, but now recognised as national terms.

THE OLD TERM	THE NEW TERM
Vulnerable adult	Adult
Perpetrator	Person alleged responsible
Safeguarding investigation	Enquiry (sometimes referred to as Section 42 enquiry)
Substantiated (allegation)	True
Unsubstantiated	Untrue
Inconclusive	Inconclusive
Protection plan	Protection plan
Institutional abuse	Organisational abuse
Serious Case Review	Safeguarding Adults Review

Defined timeframes for the completion of an enquiry are also now not required to be detailed in the SAB policy. Any enquiry should be carried out in a timely manner proportionate to the identified concerns.

Six principles of safeguarding

The Statutory guidance enshrines the six principles of safeguarding:

- **Empowerment** – there is a presumption of person-led decisions and informed consent
- **Protection** – there is support and representation for those in greatest need
- **Prevention** – it is better to take preventative action before harm occurs
- **Proportionality** – there is a proportionate and least intrusive response appropriate to the risk presented

- **Partnership** – local solutions are created through services working with their communities. Communities have a part to play in preventing, detecting and reporting neglect and abuse
- **Accountability** – accountability and transparency in delivering safeguarding.

The Act requires local authorities to widen their parameters of what constitutes abuse or neglect, recognising that abuse and neglect can take many forms. These are set out later in this chapter.

Making safeguarding personal

The Act is a major change in practice, a move away from local authorities focusing on a process-led, tick-box culture to a person-centred approach which achieves outcomes that people want. This follows a national initiative led by the Local Government Association and the Association of Directors of Adult Social Services called Making Safeguarding Personal (MSP) which follows the edict of 'no decision about me without me'. This means that the local authority should work with the person and their family to find the right solutions to keep people safe and support them to make informed choices. All adults at risk, whether they have capacity or not, should be supported to look at all options on how to resolve the concerns and achieve the outcome they want. This may be different from the outcome the person talking to the adult believes is the correct one. However, if there is reason to believe that the concerns may affect other adults (eg those living in a care home) the duty of the local authority is to balance the wishes of the individual alongside wider considerations such as the level of risk or risk of harm to others. In this situation the need for an enquiry would override the wishes of an individual. The principles of MSP are applicable to all agencies and professions involved in safeguarding adults.

A duty to co-operate

The local authority, the police and the CCGs in the NHS must each have a Designated Safeguarding Manager (DASM) The DASM must liaise with their colleagues in other organisations, provide assistance and guidance to their organisation and monitor the progress of cases to ensure that they are dealt with as quickly as possible, consistent with a thorough and fair process. There is also a duty to co-operate placed on the local authority and its partners in fulfilling their responsibilities under the Act (Section 6). All other organisations that work with or provide care and support for adults must also co-operate with safeguarding enquiries and activity if asked to do so by the local authority. An integral part of the duty to co-operate is the duty to share information. In support of the principle of prevention, local authorities must also involve and co-operate with other agencies or bodies as it considers appropriate. These can include:

- general practitioners
- dentists
- pharmacists
- NHS hospitals
- housing, health and care providers
- fire and rescue service
- ambulance services
- prisons and probation services
- advocacy services
- representatives of service users and carers.

Safeguarding enquiries

All agencies should stress the need for preventing abuse and neglect wherever possible, enabling and supporting professionals to identify concerns at an early stage and make positive interventions, by working with the individual and families to prevent the situation deteriorating or breaking down.

Safeguarding investigations, now referred to as 'Section 42 enquires', must be proportionate and focus on what the person at risk wants as an outcome. The Section 42 enquiry is a process that can include a number of 'enquiries' or 'investigations' coordinated by the local authority under the multi-agency safeguarding procedures. These 'investigations' could include a criminal investigation, a disciplinary investigation or a serious incident investigation, for example.

The person or organisation who is the subject of the enquiry is referred to as the 'person/organisation alleged responsible'. An enquiry can range from talking through the concerns of the adult with the person/organisation alleged responsible, then reviewing the care needs of the adult, to a full enquiry and report which concludes with a decision being made on the balance of probability whether the alleged concern was 'true, not true or inconclusive'. Following the outcome of the enquiry, the local authority *must* determine what further action is necessary.

The Act specifies that the person best placed to undertake the enquiry may not be a social worker. It could be the professional who knows the person best or a professional with relevant expertise regarding the concern. If there is suspicion of criminal activity, the police will always lead the enquiry. An independent professional may undertake the enquiry if there is reason to believe that the outcome could be compromised (for a variety of reasons) should a person from the organisation undertake it. More information about undertaking safeguarding enquiries or an investigation as part of an enquiry can be found in Chapter 8.

Care leaders and the Care Act

It is important that care leaders understand the implications of the legislation regarding safeguarding as set out in the Care Act for England. The Act requires the SABs to write local policies and procedures to reflect the local arrangements and processes. Thus care leaders must ensure that the safeguarding policy within their organisation reflects the Care Act, and the local care home policy reflects the local SAB policy.

Despite legislation putting adult safeguarding on a statutory footing, the implementation and execution of the practical aspects of the Act will mostly remain a local decision, just as it was before 2015. The national requirements for care homes to adhere to and understand (some of which will already be established as good practice) include:

- all providers regulated by the CQC have a duty to report any allegations of abuse or neglect to the CQC, local authority and Clinical Commissioning Group where the latter is the commissioner
- all providers must have clear operational policies and procedures that reflect the framework set out by the SAB in consultation with them. This should include what circumstances would require them to make a report outside of their own organisation to the local authority. The SAB policy should clearly identify which agencies must be notified of a safeguarding concern
- the local authority and other commissioners of care should only use safeguarding procedures in a way that reflects the principles of safeguarding and *not* as a means of intimidating providers or families
- care homes should expect regulating authorities to demonstrate transparency, open-mindedness and timeliness in order to operate fair and effective safeguarding enquiries
- care homes should expect commissioners to encourage an open culture around safeguarding, working in partnership with providers to ensure the best outcome for the adult
- care homes can expect CQC and commissioners to use alternative means of raising standards of service, including support for staff training, contractual compliance and, in the case of CQC, enforcement powers as an alternative to a safeguarding enquiry
- if a local authority has reasonable cause to suspect an adult may be experiencing, or is at risk of, abuse or neglect, they are under a duty to make (or cause another organisation to make) whatever enquiries they think necessary to decide what, if any, action needs to be taken and by whom

- the local authority will normally ask the provider involved to undertake the enquiry (assuming that there is only one enquiry). The provider will thus be asked to undertake the enquiry into any concerns unless there is a compelling reason why it is inappropriate or unsafe due to concerns about their competency to do so. The organisation's enquiry could be complemented by an enquiry by another agency, or the local authority reviewing, for example, the resident's care plan themselves
- once the enquiry is complete, the care home must notify the outcome to the local authority, which must satisfy itself that the provider's response has been sufficient to deal with the safeguarding issue. If the local authority is not satisfied it must undertake an enquiry of its own and ensure there is appropriate follow up (for example referral to CQC or professional regulators)
- any suspected criminal offence must be urgently reported to the police.
- the care home (as an employer) has a duty not only to the adult, but also a responsibility to take action in relation to an employee where allegations are made against them. Employers should ensure their disciplinary procedures are compatible with their responsibility to protect adults at risk of abuse or neglect:
  - all staff must have safeguarding training relevant to their role
  - staff undertaking an enquiry must receive suitable training
  - all organisations must have a whistleblowing policy
  - all organisations must have an information sharing protocol and policy
  - all organisations must work within the requirements of the Mental Capacity Act 2005.

The legislation supporting adults at risk in Scotland

The Adult Support and Protection (Scotland) Act was passed by the Scottish Parliament in February 2007. Part 1 of the Act, which deals with the support and protection of adults at risk of harm, came into effect in October 2008.

The Act provides greater protection to adults at risk of harm by providing powers to investigate and take action to support and protect an adult in situations where concern exists. It places a duty on specified organisations to co-operate in investigating suspected or actual harm and places a duty on councils to make enquiries and investigations to find out whether or not further action is required to stop or prevent harm occurring.

The Act also contains a range of protection orders including assessment orders, removal orders and banning orders; and ensures there are local multi-agency Adult Protection Committees across Scotland.

The definition of an adult at risk in Scotland

Adults at risk are adults, aged 16 years of age and over, who:

- are unable to safeguard their own well-being, property, rights or other interests
- are at risk of harm
- because they are affected by disability, mental disorder, illness or physical or mental infirmity, they are more vulnerable to being harmed than adults who are not so affected.

An adult is at risk of harm if:

- another person's conduct is causing (or is likely to cause) the adult to be harmed, or
- the adult is engaging (or is likely to engage) in conduct which causes (or is likely to cause) self-harm.

The overarching principle is that any intervention in an individual's affairs should provide benefit to the individual, and should be the least restrictive option of those that are available which will meet the purpose of the intervention. The intervention should take into account the wishes and feelings of the adult at risk (past and present) and the views of other significant individuals, such as the adult's nearest relative. The Act also requires the individual to be supported to take an active part in the adult protection process and to provide the adult with the relevant information and support to enable them to participate as fully as possible, regardless of their abilities, background, gender, sexual orientation etc.

Duty to make enquiries

Councils have a statutory duty to make enquiries about a person's wellbeing, property or financial affairs if they know, or believe, that the person is an adult at risk and that they might need to intervene to take protective action. Additionally, council officers have the power to carry out investigations through visits and interviews and through examination of financial or other records. Health records can only be examined by a health professional. As part of the enquiry health professionals have the power to carry out medical examinations. However, adults have the right not to answer any questions and to refuse to be medically examined. Thus a person cannot be forced to undergo an examination. Councils have a duty to consider the importance of the provision of appropriate services to the adult, including, in particular, independent advocacy.

Duty to co-operate

There is a statutory duty of co-operation for certain public bodies and their office holders to co-operate in adult safeguarding. These include councils, The health board, police and the Care Inspectorate. These public bodies must co-operate with a council making enquiries under the Act and report the facts and circumstances to the local council when they know or believe that someone is an adult at risk of harm and that action is needed to protect that adult from harm. It is an offence to prevent or obstruct any person from doing anything they are authorised to do under the Act. It is also an offence to refuse, without reasonable excuse, to comply with a request to provide information made under the provisions for the examination of records. This offence does not apply to the adult at risk.

Protection orders

The Act allows a council to apply to a sheriff for a protection order, for assessment, removal or a banning or temporary banning order. The sheriff may only grant an assessment order if satisfied the adult needs to be taken to a more suitable place in order to conduct an interview and/or a medical examination in private. A removal order can only be granted for up to seven days, if an adult is likely to be seriously harmed if not moved to a place of safety. A banning order (or temporary banning order) to protect the adult who has suffered abuse can be placed on the person responsible. This bans the subject of the order from being in a specified place, or can put specified conditions on the person responsible for the abuse for up to six months.

Protection orders should not be granted without the consent of the adult, unless no other steps can be identified to safeguard the adult.

Safeguarding in Wales

Local authorities have lead strategic responsibility for adult protection in Wales. This is set out in the document *In Safe Hands* which is the guidance of the local authorities Social Services Act 9 (1970).

Adult safeguarding in Wales currently operates using the *Wales Policy and Procedures for the Protection of Vulnerable Adults from Abuse* (Adult Protection Fora 2013) as the guide to safeguarding work of all those concerned with the welfare of vulnerable adults employed in the statutory, third (voluntary) and private sectors, in health, social care, the police and other services. Accordingly, adult protection should operate in the context of fully engaged citizenship, not restricted to social care, health services and the criminal justice system.

Adult protection in Wales has six values and rights which underpin the way vulnerable adults should be supported and cared for in whatever settings or places they live in or use:

- **Independence** – to think, act and make decisions, even when this involves a level of risk
- **Dignity** – recognition that everyone is unique, with intrinsic value as a person
- **Respect** – for a person's needs, wishes, preferences, language, race, religion and culture
- **Equality** – the right of people to be treated no less favourably than others because of their age, gender, disability, sexual orientation, religion, class, culture, language, race, ethnic origin or other relevant distinctions
- **Privacy** – the right of the individual to be left alone or undisturbed and free from intrusion or public attention in their affairs
- **Choice** – the right to make choices, and to have the alternatives and information that enable choices to be made.

Information-sharing between agencies is of paramount importance in adult protection. Good communication, co-operation and liaison between agencies and disciplines are essential. To support this, the National Assembly for Wales has issued the Welsh Accord on the Sharing of Personal Information (www.waspi.org), enabling good information sharing.

Vulnerable adults should be supported to be part of the safeguarding process and have access to advocacy services if required.

There is an overarching Adult Protection Coordinators' Group which brings together all of the 22 local authority and health board leads for adult protection working together to enable the promotion of good and consistent practice. There is also a structure of four regional adult protection groups. There is a focus on prevention and the contribution of processes such as Keeping Safe training and on advocacy.

Safeguarding investigations

While social services or health boards are responsible for coordinating an adult protection case, and the police for leading an investigation into an alleged criminal offence, the identification, assessment, protection and care of vulnerable adults is an inter-agency responsibility.

Any investigation will be managed through the adult safeguarding process; however, there is an expectation that all investigations are independent of providers and where possible are joint (for example conducted by trained social services and health investigators NOT the provider). Additionally, the investigator from the social services department cannot be the care manager already involved in the care of the residents affected by the allegations.

Arrangements for safeguarding in Wales are likely to change as a consequence of the new Social Services and Well-being (Wales) Act 2014. Regulations to underpin the Act will be implemented in 2016.

The Act provides a new legal framework for adults at risk and provides local authorities with further duties to ensure enquiries and investigations can be undertaken when it is suspected that an adult is at risk.

In Wales an adult is at risk if:

- they are being abused or neglected, or there is a risk they will be
- they have care and support needs
- they cannot keep themselves safe from abuse or neglect.

Duties are placed on local authority partners to co-operate and provide information in relation to safeguarding. The Act also establishes a National Independent Safeguarding Board to replace the current structure. This board will provide national support and advice to ensure the effectiveness of the local safeguarding boards. The Act requires the local authority to undertake enquiries, holding the person at risk central to the enquiry, ensuring the response is proportionate and in keeping with the person's wishes. The Act also allows the local authority to make an application to the magistrates court for an adult protection and support order. This enables the local authority to go into a building with a police officer to see the person, speak in private to the person, assess if the person is making their own choices and make decisions about whether the person should be removed.

Safeguarding in Northern Ireland

Safeguarding adults in Northern Ireland is currently undertaken following the guidance in the Adult Safeguarding Northern Ireland regional and local partnership arrangements (2010).

There are two tiers of safeguarding partnerships:

1. the regional body - the Northern Ireland Adult Safeguarding Partnership (NIASP)
2. the local bodies - the five Local Adult Safeguarding Partnerships (LASPs).

In summary, the NIASP will determine the strategy for safeguarding vulnerable adults, develop and disseminate guidance and operational policies and procedures, monitor trends and outcomes and monitor and evaluate the effectiveness of partnership arrangements.

In broad terms the LASPs will facilitate practice, including engagement with service users, families and carers and the wider public, at a local level. The focus of safeguarding work is balancing safeguarding with the right to autonomy and self-determination, securing meaningful consent, assessing mental capacity and assessing and managing risk. There is an important emphasis in adult safeguarding work on empowerment which enables people whose situation makes them vulnerable to keep themselves safe.

New legislation

In November 2014, The Northern Ireland Executive drafted a new adult safeguarding policy which seeks to improve outcomes for adults considered to be at risk of harm, by promoting preventative practice and robust protection responses where they are required. The draft policy is underpinned by a set of principles that recognise an adult's fundamental right to make informed, supported choices about how they want to live their life.

The outcome of this national policy will determine how adult safeguarding is conducted in Northern Ireland in the future.

Suggested good practice for care leaders across the UK

For some care leaders, new legislation in any of the home nations reinforces the local authorities' established practice, while for others, it will be a new approach to safeguarding.

It is clear from the summaries of adult safeguarding across the UK that, despite some local differences, the principles of adult safeguarding are similar wherever a care leader is working. Alongside ensuring the legal obligations are met, as set out above, there are additional activities which the leader might undertake in order to develop the best possible engagement with adult safeguarding. Set out below are some suggestions which may apply across the UK, or may be specific to one nation:

- have a copy of your country's current national legislation and guidance
- keep up to date with local legislation development
- know the name and contact details of the local authority, CCG/health board and police Designated Safeguarding Managers
- appoint a Designated Safeguarding Manager for your care home or organisation

- find out if the SAB has a care provider representative as part of the membership and arrange regular meetings with them
- contact your care home provider representative organisation and ensure any local information about safeguarding is received
- volunteer to be on a SAB sub-group
- talk to commissioners and gain an detailed understanding of what they consider a safeguarding concern in accordance with local policy
- ensure the care home directors and owners understand how safeguarding works in the locality
- obtain the contact details of the local advocacy service
- review all policies and procedures to ensure the six principles of safeguarding apply to all aspects of care and practice
- embrace the golden thread of safeguarding throughout all activities in the care home
- register for regular newsletters from organisations who provide information about safeguarding, for example the Disclosure and Barring Service and Social Care Institute of Excellence (SCIE)
- review the organisation's or home's quality assurance processes to ensure they reflect and include safeguarding aspects as part of all routine reviews undertaken.

By undertaking some or all of the best practice ideas set out above, the care leader will be prepared for the likely eventuality that local authorities and CCGs will start building tighter safeguarding aspects into their commissioning, contracting processes and quality assurance processes.

POINTERS FOR PREVENTION OF ABUSE

1 Primary prevention
General activities, for example...

Find the appropriate website and register to receive updates on the safeguarding legislation, development and implementation.

2 Secondary prevention
Specific activities, for example...

Build relationships with commissioners and contract managers and call them to discuss issues to develop trust and mutual understanding.

3 Tertiary prevention
A response to an actual situation, for example...

If a safeguarding concern requires investigation, undertake an enquiry that is impartial, objective and transparent, or agree ways of working with the local authority safeguarding enquiry officer which demonstrate your desire to be open, objective and transparent.

Chapter 3
Caring is a privilege, not a right

For some people who care for adults at risk, the desire to help, support and improve people's lives is a vocation. It is a feeling that cannot easily be articulated, but lies deep within the person. Taking on a caring role is a life plan and another career path is not an option.

For many other people, however, entering the caring professions happens for a variety of reasons. Some need time to realise their ambitions or discover them through personal or life experience, and others take on the caring role to meet family commitments, because it fits with their lifestyle, for convenience or simply because they need a job. It would be unusual to find a person entering the caring profession because of the potential to earn lots of money!

There can be few who deliberately set out to abuse, so why does it happen? The reasons are complex. Low pay, long hours, poor working conditions and staff shortages, together possibly with a focus by employers on money to the detriment of care, are often cited as contributing factors in organisational neglect and abuse (Mid Staffordshire, Georgiou 2014, Killett, Bowes *et al* 2012).

The good news is that although these factors are present in many care environments, proportionately few care settings are found to be abusive. This suggests that there are other factors that prevent a care setting becoming abusive.

In the health service, unregistered nursing assistants make up around a third of the care workforce, while in social care, the majority of staff are unregistered (Cavendish 2013). Would there be benefits, therefore, in having a registration scheme for care support staff? The debate continues. It is unclear whether the driving force is to ensure a worker's practice can be regulated (and the worker stopped working if necessary) or if it is to assist in raising the status of a currently unregulated workforce and improving their self-worth.

At a local level, leaders in any care setting need to be able to demonstrate to the whole team that the contribution each member makes is valuable. Such support for every member will help to overcome some of the challenges. It requires thought being given to the type of work being undertaken. Perhaps, the work is considered 'basic', and registered nurses working in a care environment express the opinion that they cannot, or will not, work directly to deliver care to the residents because they would have to work as a 'carer'. Equally the leader may hear mutterings that the staff are reluctant to engage with residents to carry out social activities because these are the responsibility of the activity co-ordinator. To be in a position to counteract these views, the leader needs to be able to articulate what caring is, as well as set clear parameters about what is expected of each care team member whatever their professional role.

What is fundamental care?

Fundamental care is the care that needs to be delivered to maintain those essentials of life which meet the needs of each person. These needs are described in Maslow's 'hierarchy of needs' as those required to support each person physically, emotionally and spiritually. In ritualistic care settings, this is often drilled down to the simplest descriptors of eating, drinking, toileting, and is considered 'basic care'. This approach to care can cause staff delivering the care to feel devalued. It also underestimates the skills required to carry out the work in a professional and caring manner.

In the care sector, the refrain "I am only a carer" is too commonly heard (Cavendish 2013), and the notion that caring is simple is reinforced by the simplistic language used in documents such as the NHS Continuing Care Decision Support Tool (DH 2012), which describes activities as simple and routine. The term 'basic care' dramatically understates the work of care staff (Cavendish 2013) and the use of such language then reinforces the view that 'anyone' can give care and 'anyone' can do it. Leaders should help staff recognise and value the contribution they make to a person's life by reinforcing the privileged position they have in being able to affect so closely the life of another human being. This requires the leader to deconstruct or break down an apparently simple action, help the care worker explore what they did and how they did it, and then to reconstruct the activity to demonstrate the complexity of the care that has been delivered to the person (RCN 2004).

Helping a person go to the toilet, get washed and dressed, eat, walk about, sleep well, keep warm, feel contented and valued, and engage in quality, fulfilling activities while also giving the person a sense of hope, are all part of fundamental care and are often not simple. The complexity will depend on the residents' health, their physical and mental abilities, their level of cognition and the nature of their life experiences. By helping the care worker to see the person as they were before they entered the home, the leader can reinforce the sense of privilege for every care worker in being able to support even the most challenging resident.

The leader should act as a role model in everything they do. The privilege of working with adults at risk should be emphasised to care staff, but also to every member of the team including the chefs, kitchen staff, housekeepers and support staff. Everyone who works in a care setting has the opportunity to positively influence and support the life and wellbeing of the residents, and the leader should encourage the whole team to take pride in the contribution they make.

The privilege of working with adults at risk

One issue identified during the investigation into organisational abuse at Orchid View (Georgiou 2014) was that there was low local unemployment causing difficulties for the home in recruiting and retaining nursing and other care staff. At interview in such areas there may be a perception among prospective applicants that the care setting needs them more than the applicant needs the job. By contrast, in other areas where unemployment is high, applicants may be plentiful and very keen to fill the post. In both cases the attitude of the applicant to the work and the people they will be caring for must remain central to the decision to recruit. The applicant does not have 'a right' to the job, but the resident does have 'a right' to kind and caring staff, who are able to deliver the sort of care that is required. Embedding the cultural view as early as possible that the new recruit is privileged to have been chosen to support the residents will help to reinforce the belief that caring is a privilege, not a right.

The privilege of learning the necessary care skills to work with adults at risk

Every care worker should understand that it is a privilege to work with adults to learn and craft the required skills in a caring manner. There are over 1.3 million frontline staff who are not registered nurses who deliver hands-on care in hospitals, care homes and homes of individuals (Cavendish 2013). All those staff should feel privileged and proud that they have been chosen and have the skills necessary to support frail and vulnerable people.

The privilege of being a registered health and social care professional

Before they can practise, health and social care professionals are required to register with their professional regulator, each of which has a Code of Practice, the rule book with the required rules or standards. Each professional is then obliged either to produce evidence of continued professional development or testify that they are continuing to develop their practice in order to continue to be registered. Being registered as a health and social care professional effectively gives the person a licence to practice. The licence can be revoked at any time:

- if the professional does not re-register
- by due process, if referred to the professional conduct committee of their regulator
- if they obtain a criminal conviction for certain criminal acts.

Most professionals understand these facts but may not have considered them in any depth. In particular they may not have considered what having a licence to practice really means in respect of 'accountability' and 'responsibility', terms often used by nurses and other health care and social care professionals without perhaps knowing how to put them into practice.

In safeguarding, there can be occasions when the leader must consider whether a professional has complied with their code of practice. If the leader feels the worker has not, a referral to their appropriate professional body should be made. It is natural that the leader may feel anxious about making such a referral and having to take responsibility for the referral perhaps affecting the health and social care professional's livelihood. However it is the duty of the leader to make the referral and it is the regulator who will be the one making the decision as to whether the person should lose their licence to practice. The leader needs to hold on to the belief, at all times, that the purpose of registration is to protect the public.

A useful analogy is the right to hold a driving licence. The person is entitled to drive a car provided they both have a licence and comply with the relevant motoring laws and conditions of the road. If the driver breaches any law or standards set out in the Highway Code or legislation, they must accept personal responsibility for their actions even if they did not mean to break the law. The driver who breaks the speed limit cannot claim that it was their boss who told them to hurry, they must accept personal responsibility for their own actions and their own decisions to breach the laws of the road, and they must accept whatever sanction is applicable. Special mitigation may be considered but it would never be allowed to justify the actions.

So leaders must ensure that registered health and social care professionals understand that their licence to practice is a privilege not a right. For their part the professionals must accept personal responsibility for their actions and ensure that they work within the rules of their particular profession.

Managers of care homes may be registered professionals, but they also may not be. The legal duty, though, for all registered managers to ensure residents are cared for correctly does have legal consequences – prosecution as the registered manager, in England and Wales, can and does occur. The range of duties for a manager should not be underestimated, including the duty to do everything possible to protect the older person from harm. It might be thought by some that those giving direct care, whether nurses or care staff, are the only staff able to be held to account in a criminal prosecution. However, as attitudes change and the care of vulnerable people is better understood by the police and prosecution services, criminal prosecutions for neglect are increasingly being made against managers and owners, particularly under the Mental Capacity Act, using the charge of wilful neglect. In Yorkshire, for example, the manager and owner of a care home were both sentenced to 12 months in prison having been found guilty of wilful neglect. Residents suffered from pressure ulcers and neither manager or owner took action to prevent the harm, despite requests for resources from the staff (www.yorkshirepost.co.uk).

Care and support staff and their responsibilities
Although care and support staff are not registered, and are rarely left in sole charge, it is important that leaders make them aware of their responsibility to ensure residents are cared for safely. Legislation in respect of 'adults who lack capacity' and the Health and Safety at Work Act are both examples of legislation where criminal prosecution can occur against the care staff who failed to carry out an activity in accordance with:

- their training
- the care plan
- the organisation's policy and procedures
- national legislation and guidance.

The privilege of leading a team
Being the leader of a care team is such a privileged position because the leader has the ability to shape the staff, shape the culture and uphold the standards of care. It is also sometimes the most difficult position because the leader has the responsibility to:

- advise senior managers and directors or owners of organisations if the care standards are not being met
- record and report to regulatory bodies if they are concerned that residents are suffering because their organisation is not complying with its duties
- motivate and support staff while upholding their duties to residents and families

- create a climate and culture of openness and high standards
- ensure that the staff fully understand their legal duties and responsibilities, without creating an environment of fear and anxiety.

An important ingredient in ensuring cohesiveness in the team and supporting the complex care delivered by both care staff and registered professionals is 'connectedness' within the organisation, with strong, seamless lines of communication (Lupton & Croft-White 2013).

At meetings and handovers the language of celebration is a powerful tool to reinforce the notion of the privilege of caring and working with the client group. This notion can be further emphasised by ensuring the active engagement of residents and their families with staff concerning decisions about the home.

It is important to encourage staff to focus their care on the resident as a person, and not simply see the resident as an object for whom they have to complete tasks. This is all helped by encouraging staff to participate in personalisation of residents' bedrooms, memory books, personal hobbies, or new interests, as well as resident participation in social events and encouraging residents' families to become actively involved.

EXAMPLE

Arthur had dementia and was visited regularly by his daughter and wife in a care home where he lived. One day his daughter took him blackberry - picking in the grounds. The care assistant who came from overseas had never seen blackberries and did not know they could be eaten. So Arthur's wife baked Arthur and the care assistant a blackberry and apple crumble. The care assistant was thrilled and felt privileged that he could share this experience with Arthur. He not only learnt more about Arthur but he also learnt more about the country in which he worked.

Other helpful actions to reinforce the notion of how privileged it is to care include:

- supporting staff to write person-centred care plans together with care staff of all grades, followed by reviewing them and identifying care needs
- creating a key worker system can also be helpful but there must be clear guidelines about what the key worker does - merely requiring the worker to check if the person needs more toiletries, for example, will reinforce the tasks element involved in caring but will do nothing to emphasise the privilege of caring
- key workers and registered professionals being encouraged to build a relationship with a resident's whole family and develop an understanding of the resident as a person
- leaders encouraging staff to share some of themselves with residents, if it is safe and appropriate

to do so. Common interests are a safe topic and during their discussion the resident becomes more human to a care worker.

The leader has a crucial role in ensuring that all levels of the organisation have positive attitudes towards adults at risk. Although it may sometimes be a challenge, a leader should not allow senior managers or directors to use language and/or conduct themselves in a way that has an obvious and negative influence on staff. The attitude of managers at every level of an organisation has a crucial influence on the attitude of frontline staff and their level of engagement (PANICOA). When the senior management and organisational attitudes are negative, the risk of organisational abuse becomes heightened (Georgiou 2014).

Supporting staff at difficult times

For all staff there will be times and incidents which cause them difficulties or are challenging to handle. A good leader recognises the limits of the responsibilities of different staff and reassures them there will be no loss of face if they seek help from the leader sooner rather than later. A positive culture of care includes supporting staff in difficult relationships or when there have been negative interactions with residents or relatives as sometimes happens (Lupton & Croft-White 2013).

POINTERS FOR PREVENTION OF ABUSE

1 Primary prevention
General activities, for example...

Put a weekly poster on display for staff to write 'examples of 'what made me proud today.'

2 Secondary prevention
Specific activities, for example...

Support the team to develop a list of banned words and phrases that are organisational or negative towards the residents.

3 Tertiary prevention
A response to an actual situation, for example...

If there is an incident where a staff member ignores a resident, or puts them down or shows disrespect, a leader helps the staff member to recognise why their action was inappropriate. Instead, the knowledge, skill and experience they should be using is encouraged so that they can build pride in themselves and their care.

Chapter 4
Being proud of your profession and supporting your team to be proud

The right qualifications for the job

The qualifications, skills and experience of leaders in care homes can vary enormously. A positive, successful care home is usually led by a positive, strong and confident leader. It is unusual to find organisational abuse in care homes where the leaders are skilled, knowledgeable and clear about how residents should be supported.

In the past, care homes with nursing had a matron who was a registered nurse. In some homes this worked well as the matron had the right combination of clinical skills, management and leadership skills, and expertise in the speciality of caring in a care home setting. However, being registered does not necessarily mean a nurse will have the managerial and leadership skills required to be a great manager. The role might not suit a person who might be clinically sound in a hospital but cannot apply these skills in a care home setting, or has little understanding of the unique speciality of care in a care home, or of the challenges involved in providing quality of life alongside quality of care..

The risk is that the lack of these skills can lead to chaotic, disorganised care and systems, and power struggles and dissatisfaction for staff and residents, which in turn can leave the home at high risk of developing an abusive culture (Georgiou 2014).

So, in many homes which have given full consideration to the qualities needed to manage the home and lead the clinical team, the home leader or manager may not be a registered nurse, opening up the opportunity for two sets of staff to work together in the best interests of the residents.

Good care leaders may 'grow up through the ranks' and learn from experience. They will acquire the appropriate qualifications in care and management which have become increasingly recognised as an integral part of the skill and knowledge base required. Qualifications give a professional the confidence to believe in themselves and are external recognition that a set standard has been achieved. Just as it is a mistake to assume that a registered nurse is an ideal person to manage a care home, it is worth considering leaders who have a vocational, academic or social care qualification in leadership provided, of course, their attitude, experiences and vision are appropriate.

The self-confidence, skills, knowledge and experience shown by a leader should be celebrated by the senior managers and directors of an organisation; but they should not assume the leader knows all the answers, or has the competence or confidence to deal with all situations. Leaders need support and continuing professional development throughout their career, and investment in them will significantly contribute to the quality of the home.

Leaders who have worked hard to gain qualifications should be given opportunities to use all their skills, and should be openly praised for their expertise. Senior managers and directors must ensure they value the contribution of the various skills and qualifications leaders may have, and appreciate that one size does not necessarily have to fit all.

EXAMPLE

A residential care home run by a charity had, for 40 years, had a registered nurse as the manager. A new chief executive appointed a new manager who had a social care qualification. A senior manager in the organisation openly referred to the new manager as 'only being a carer', immediately undermining the position of the manager and damaging the pride and confidence she had in herself and her expertise. Cultural change was needed both in the home and at senior management level.

Valuing the team

The tone set by the leader has a direct impact on the quality of care and the culture of the home. Demonstrating that s/he values the team is not simply about offering them good pay, a flexible duty rota or fair holiday entitlement. There is strong evidence that care improves when all staff feel valued as part of a strong, self-reinforcing team (Cavendish 2013). Staff at all levels should be treated as part of the team, a problem that has shown itself in the NHS which tends to treat care assistants and the registered nurses who supervise them as separate work forces (Cavendish 2013). In some care homes the same mistakes are made, for example not allowing care assistants to write in care records or give information at handovers.

The structure of the team

The culture of the team and how all members are valued influences the pride they take in themselves and in turn the pride they take in caring for residents. Team structures can be complicated with numerous variables but, for simplicity, there are basically two team structures, a pyramid or a jigsaw.

The **pyramid** structure has a clear hierarchy with the directors and senior managers at the top, the home manager below and the care staff further down the 'pecking order'. In some homes administration and business management staff are seen as 'more important' or senior to care staff. At the bottom of the pyramid are the invisible staff, those who work in the background, the kitchen and laundry staff and the cleaning work force. Apart from mandatory training, for them opportunities for training are often few and far between, and the conversation about how to improve the wellbeing of residents rarely involves these members of staff.

Conversely the structure may be 'a **jigsaw** model. Every person who has any involvement with the resident and their family is part of that jigsaw. Everyone has a part to play and everyone's contribution is as important as the next. For example the chief executive must ensure the organisation is sound and that there is clear strategic direction without which the organisation could collapse and the residents be made homeless. Similarly maintenance staff have a role in ensuring the home is well maintained and that everything works, while the kitchen assistant has an equally vital role in supporting the chef in food preparation, washing cooking utensils and crockery and interacting with the residents. If the kitchen assistant does not take pride in her/his work the risk of infection becomes very high and the risk of harm to the residents inevitable. Within this system a positive leader will ensure everyone in the team knows and takes pride in the contribution they make to the residents' health, safety and wellbeing.

Within an overarching team structure there will be sub-groups and sub-structures. The leader needs to understand what official teams work within the home, but also the unofficial structures that may develop. It requires a skilful and assertive leader to stop or reduce the development of unofficial negative structures which have a negative impact on residents' care.

A sub-structure could include a team who like to work together on the same shift to the exclusion of others. It may benefit the residents to have a group with a close working relationship, but the group may also develop ways of working that suit the team rather than the residents. Cliques, which exclude some staff, can spring up to the detriment of all. Excessive familiarity and complacency make it hard for staff to challenge and report bad practice and poor attitudes. As well as the closed group, some staff may also develop their own hierarchy based on length of service, age or whether they are full or part time. Some staff may use this power to influence less assertive or confident staff. And if they are happy to exert power over colleagues it is likely they will use similar techniques with residents.

Leaders should also be aware of how key personnel can control the home subversively, if they are not resident centred, and do not consider themselves an equal part of the team. A chef may decide s/he doesn't have time to cook a special meal, or maintenance staff could cause delay to care staff taking residents out for a walk by postponing the routine maintenance of a wheelchair, or a carer could exclude a resident from an activity by taking too long to get them ready, thus preventing the activity co-ordinator from doing their job.

Staff who do not feel valued either stay but are easily dissatisfied and engage poorly with residents, or they leave to find work where they feel more valued. Staff turnover or 'churn' has been reported to have a rate of 19% a year in care homes and up to 30% a year in domiciliary care (Cavendish 2013). The reasons are wide and varied, but unhappiness because staff do not feel valued is an important factor to consider when addressing recruitment issues. It is no surprise that high staff turnover and frequent changes in management are risk factors for organisational abuse. Care businesses should have robust plans to recruit and sustain a trained workforce and the damaging impact of a home not having a registered manager should be closely risk managed (Georgiou 2014).

Supporting the team to take a pride in their profession

If the team feels proud about the contribution they make to the residents' care and the pride the leader has in them, they will be more confident in speaking up if they have concerns about abuse and other matters. There are a number of initiatives that can support staff to have a pride in themselves and their work:

- **Internal staff award.** Larger care companies have award ceremonies to recognise staff that have done good work. It is important these awards are open to all staff, and it is vital that families and residents are invited to nominate members of staff who they feel would make worthy winners. It is worth highlighting that some staff groups may be hidden from residents by the nature of their work, yet they still do a vital job and may have gone 'above and beyond' their role to help a resident or their family.
- **National Care Awards.** An organisation feels an immense sense of pride when a staff member is shortlisted for a National Care Award. Even the simple act of nominating staff (and telling them) gives a powerful message that they are valued and their hard work has not gone unnoticed. Be sure to consider the awards for support staff and not only care staff. A leader may be in an ideal position to nominate a senior manager who has gone that extra mile. Nominating a person for an award sends powerful messages of pride, gratitude and confidence that cannot always be said in other ways.
- **Attending ceremonies and conferences.** Leaders can show pride in the team from any department by enabling representatives, whenever possible, to attend award ceremonies, conferences or functions, bringing residents with them if practical to represent the home.

- **Social functions at the home.** Ensure there are representatives from all departments at meetings to plan social functions. They will be able to bring new and different perspectives and ideas from the team they represent but also suggest how their department can contribute to the function. Individual staff may have 'hidden talents' not known to the home leader which could be unearthed. The department representative will be able to encourage the team they work with to be more involved in a practical way or, at the very least, to know what is going on.

Training and development for all staff

Because of the nature of care work it is easier to identify the training needs of staff that provide direct care for residents rather than it is for support staff. Yet support staff can have an impact that is just as equally positive or negative on residents as direct care teams and their training needs must be fulfilled.

It is also important a leader does not assume that simply because a new worker has got a relevant qualification they automatically know the attitudes, attributes and culture of care that is expected at their new care home. Rash assumptions can lead to serious mistakes.

The leader should ensure that all staff are trained in how the home expects residents to be treated and supported. The principles of person-centred care, initially developed in respect to people living with dementia, are now used when supporting all residents, regardless of diagnosis. The culture and attitudes required of staff can be set out in an education and development module focusing on person-centred care. The leader should ensure all staff, regardless of position or experience, take this core module when they start work in the home or organisation.

Specialist modules should be developed and offered for the different roles staff play in the life of the care home; it should never be assumed that person-centred care only applies to direct care. The AgeCare Award (Phair & Benson 2003) is a good example of an accredited BTeC Certificate in the care and support of older people. The award has four care modules that all staff complete, regardless of position or grade in the organisation. The fifth module is specific to the individual's role within the home. One such module, for example, is for chefs who are asked to look at how they can work with residents in a person-centred way, with activities including residents' involvement in menu planning and arranging private meals and birthday celebrations. Housekeepers complete a unit that not only looks at appropriate cleaning methods, but requires house-keepers to undertake a room housekeeping assessment with a resident. The focus is to establish how the resident wants their room to be cleaned, particularly personal furniture and ornaments. Most modules require multi-disciplinary interaction and joint discussions. Registered nurses sit alongside cleaners and kitchen assistants, each staff group learning to value each other and taking pride in their own contribution to the residents' care. This approach includes giving housekeepers the confidence to feel they can report any small concern they might have noticed when in the residents' rooms (for example blood on a sheet or uneaten food) and thus feeling part of the team. This is an example of connectedness (choice) where all of those involved in the home have a sense of community, empowering all staff to take responsibility within defined boundaries for the contributions they make to residents' care. This not only improves the pride staff have in themselves, but improves residents' experiences and the quality and consistency of care (choice) they receive.

How the team can help solve concerns

Some concerns expressed by relatives or residents can appear minor to the leader, but may be a significant indicator of poor care as far as the family is concerned. These concerns need to be addressed as soon as possible. However simple solutions may not work if the whole team do not feel the solutions proposed are practical. If not resolved, a small problem can escalate to a dispro-portionate size and could be an indicator that other perhaps larger areas of concern are not being addressed.

EXAMPLE

Bert went through a phase of ripping buttons off his shirts, but the reason for his behaviour could not be established. His daughter suggested she would give him a steady supply of shirts from the local charity shops, and his wife asked that the shirts should be thrown away when ripped. The family became increasingly upset, then annoyed and eventually very angry because Bert continued to be dressed in ripped shirts. In the end the family reported the care home to social services as they began to believe it was a sign of poor care and a symptom of weak leadership.

When the concern was explored it became evident that Bert was being cared for in an undignified way because everyone was too task-focused to think about or communicate how he might feel sitting in a ripped shirt. Care staff dressed him in clothes taken from the wardrobe in the morning. In the evening the night staff put all clothes in the laundry and the next day the laundry worker washed all the clothes including the ripped shirts. The housekeeper then ironed all the clean clothes, including the ripped shirts, and put them back in the wardrobe. The manager had told one staff member that the daughter would provide more shirts and that the ripped ones should be thrown away, but the message was never transferred to the rest of the team even though the manager walked the home daily. She never even noticed Bert in his ripped shirts.

Supporting all staff to take pride in the contribution they make to residents' wellbeing, and giving each one of them the confidence to notice, think and suggest actions to support residents is vital for reinforcing the value the leader places on all the staff, thus improving the quality of care.

Upholding standards and motivating good practice

The leader of the team must lead by example, the most valuable qualities shown being passion and determination to ensure residents receive the best care. There are many ways for a leader to monitor, audit and quality assure standards of care which then give her/him the opportunities to thank and praise staff on the one hand or identify areas of concern requiring remedial action. While it is vital that the leader is clear and unambiguous about the standards that are expected, equally s/he must be willing to listen to reasons why something cannot be done and encourage staff to contribute problem-solving suggestions.

If a leader is sure that an action or development of a new system is in the residents' best interests, they must have the courage to stay firm despite hurdles which may have to be overcome or compromises made due to logistical or financial constraints. Equally the leader will also need to have the courage to inform senior managers within the organisation – or even speak to external agencies - if they feel actions are being taken which put residents' health and wellbeing at risk.

Routine and day-to-day monitoring by the leader – 'walking the home' – is the best way to 'nip things in the bud'. There is a fine balance between staff feeling constantly checked up on, and them feeling that their high standards are being fairly audited. What staff appreciate is the evidence of positive findings, as well as concerns, being fed back routinely and impartially. Like all teams, a home will be judged by the weakest link, so all team members need to feel that the leader is scrutinising them actively to ensure all team members are contributing to the good work. Any audits should be carried out with healthy scepticism and small details will often give a good picture of the culture of care and the pride and professional approach taken by staff. A simple walkabout can monitor the cleanliness and personal presentation of each resident, and whether each one has been encouraged to be involved in their own care. Necessary charts can be checked to ensure they exist and have been accurately completed. The odour, cleanliness and tidiness of all areas will give an indication of the overall hygiene of the home.

Care plans and records should be examined to ensure assessments have not only been carried out but have been acted on; and that any concerns noted in the records have been discussed or referred to the appropriate professional.

Participating in handovers and listening to the type of language used to describe residents and any difficulties is a good indicator of attitudes, as well as listening to casual conversation in the staff room or public areas.

Auditing other routinely gathered information can also give an indication of the quality of care being delivered. For example, accident reports can assist in identifying not only who is falling but if action following the fall was taken appropriately, and they may also give information about the type of care being delivered and by whom. Mapping the time and location of the fall can identify the staff on duty, whether it was around a meal time (was the resident hungry?) and where the fall occurred.

Large numbers of incidents involving different residents does not necessarily suggest lack of care. A home in one care group had numerous falls in one month (none serious), but they occurred in the garden, the lounge and in bedrooms while residents were engaged in activities. Another home in the same group had fewer falls in the same month, again occurring throughout the day, but all in residents' bedrooms. The leader decided to explore not only whether falls risk assessments were being followed in both homes, but why in the second home it appeared residents never left their bedrooms. The first home was demonstrating they were prepared to take risks and support residents to have a good quality of activity during the day. The second home, by contrast, was risk averse to the detriment of the residents' wellbeing.

Regular supervision, appraisal and performance management promotes a culture of learning within organisations. It allows individuals to discuss their learning needs and work actively to address these. It also enables the leader to reinforce positive practice and attitudes, praise examples of how the worker has supported or cared for residents, and discuss ways of working or improving practice. Supervision and appraisal are different systems that should come together to ensure good practice and personal and professional development.

Supervision involves regular contact between the supervisor and a care worker during which time they monitor and reflect on practice, review and prioritise work. The supervisor can provide guidance, support and identify areas of work that may need development. S/he may also wish to praise high quality work that deserves to be celebrated.

It is easy in a busy home to forget or run out of time to do supervision, but its value as part of the home's safeguarding strategy cannot be underestimated.

Appraisal is more formal, involving an evaluation of the worker over time and is usually undertaken annually (Care Council of Wales).

It is important to consider the nature of the relationship between the leader and worker outside supervision. A strong friendship, for example, could affect the leader's ability to present concerns identified during supervision or appraisal. There is a fine balance between building a positive, strong and friendly relationship with staff while at the same time maintaining the ability to take tough decisions.

POINTERS FOR PREVENTION OF ABUSE

1 Primary prevention
General activities, for example...

Write a welcome letter for all new employees, adjusting it to give them an example of the importance of their particular role to the residents.

2 Secondary prevention
Specific activities, for example...

Change the staff photo board so that it shows a circle of staff photographs, of all positions, set around a montage of photographs of residents and relatives.

3 Tertiary prevention
A response to an actual situation, for example...

Should an incident occur when a worker fails to carry out care correctly, review the attitude and understanding of the care worker regarding the value of their work, as well as thinking carefully about the retraining they will need to improve their practice.

Chapter 5
Care, kindness and compassion

The importance of care and compassion in delivering care in health and social care settings has become a frequently raised issue within the context of reports about neglect or failed care. The often repeated question is: why are nurses and care staff no longer caring and compassionate? Broad-sweeping statements made in the media give weight to the belief that everyone working in health and social care has lost the ability to be kind, considerate and caring. Reports such as the *Serious Case Review* for Orchid View care home and the Mid Staffordshire NHS Foundation Trust public enquiry made national headlines. Investigative programmes, such as the BBC *Panorama* programme 'Behind Closed Doors' (2014), reinforce this public view.

Some care home professionals are able to give a balanced response to how widespread the problems are. Others, however, are defensive. They cite the reasons why the neglect might occur, condemn the publicity as damaging to the care industry (Hayes & Whitney 2014) and attempt to play down continued scandals of poor care and neglect, arguing there is excellent care in many care homes.

The reality is that the actions of some staff and organisations have damaged the reputation of all nurses and care staff in the whole industry. The gift, however, of changing this perception sits not only with the media, who rarely report positive news stories, but with the care industry itself. National leaders should condemn organisations or individual homes that bring the industry into disrepute by not tolerating or allowing such organisations to be seen to represent the values of the industry.

At a local level, individual leaders can work to ensure the care delivered in their care home is caring and compassionate, whether the resident is supported by the care staff, the cook or the maintenance person, and that the care leader helps staff to recognise care and compassion and celebrate it. These values will create care homes which their communities will recognise as places where they would want their relatives to be cared for.

What are care and compassion?

The words care and compassion are used constantly but are not so easily defined. Residents know when staff have been kind, they can feel the benefits of it, though they may be less able to describe exactly what it was that made the difference.

Compassion revolves around the way people relate to each other (Dewar 2013), the invisibility of small acts that are simple not clever, basic not abstruse, peripheral not central (Pearson 2006). It is often only when these acts are missing and a negative impact is felt as a result that kind or compassionate acts are better understood. Chochinor (2007) defined compassion as "a deep awareness of the suffering of another coupled with a wish to relieve it". This type of definition suggests that care staff only show compassion to relieve suffering thus reacting to a situation. Dewar (2013) suggests that compassion is a response to vulnerability in others, which reflects compassion in practice. She says the key interpersonal processes that are needed to achieve compassionate, relationship-focused care include:

• engaging in conversation with patients to understand better who they are and what matters to them
• engaging in conversation to know how patients feel about their experience of care
• working together with patients to shape the way things are done.

Other research by Margreat Van de Cingel (2011) with older people concluded that compassion is a process that has seven dimensions:

1. **Attention** – consciously showing an interest in whatever is important to the other person (for example, a resident in a care home)
2. **Listening** – active listening by encouraging the other person to tell their story
3. **Confronting** – listening to the expressed suffering by the resident and reflecting back that it is 'ok' for them to feel the way they do. Staff are encouraged to recognise and allow the resident to express their feelings
4. **Involvement** – staff recognise the patient's emotion and are just as concerned about the resident as the resident her/himself
5. **Helping** – simply giving someone a hand. Small actions can make the biggest difference
6. **Presence** – being there, quietly supporting the person emotionally
7. **Understanding** – ensuring the resident feels the staff are trying to understand what is happening to them.

The above positive statements show behaviours that demonstrate compassion, but the reasons why compassion is sometimes absent in care settings are more widely disputed. Patterson *et al* in Dewar (2013) describe current care cultures as adopting a "perform or perish" model characterised by weak leadership, a punitive culture and an emphasis on the task rather than the process. They suggest that this model creates impoverished care environments which are less likely to achieve high quality care and that kindness and compassion will only occur if the environment and working conditions are favourable and meet the staff's needs.

While the link between the attitude of managers, the organisational culture and their terms and conditions at work will have an impact on staff morale, it appears to be too simplistic to directly link lack of compassion with external factors alone. After all, compassion can be seen on a daily basis when watching news reports of disasters or conflict around the world. Volunteers, workers and affected individuals help each other and try to show kindness and compassion. Here the essence of compassion is kindness and a desire to help a fellow human being, or to be simply 'nice' to one another.

The culture of an organisation impacts directly on how much staff feel valued or cared for. It sets standards of how care is viewed and whether all staff understand the need to show kindness and compassion. The Department of Health in England responded to the issue of poor care and neglect at Mid Staffordshire NHS Foundation Trust by publishing a three-year policy called Compassion in Practice (NHS Commissioning Board 2012) which proposes to develop a culture of compassionate practice by setting out a shared vision, a set of values and proposed actions.

The vision is not explicit but the document does introduce six fundamental values, the '6 Cs' of:

1. Care
2. Compassion
3. Competence
4. Communication
5. Courage
6. Commitment.

A critical review of the document and the 6Cs initiative by Dewar & Christley (2013) identifies a number of concerns with the policy. They claim the 6Cs are reductionist and simplistic, and because the policy only involves nurses it excludes other direct and indirect staff involved in the care of residents.

Other commentators take the view that the very reason for the increased dispassionate care currently noticed is that more and more directives are being introduced to try and enforce a caring attitude by reducing it to a task, for example requiring nurses to ask every patient "Is there anything I can do for you?" every hour, which takes away the inner moral act of wanting to help (Cuthbert

2013). It may be that the increasingly casual callousness of nursing and care services merely reflect a broader (societal) shift in the perception of individuals.

What kindness and compassion look like in reality

Kindness and compassion are not just about what is done but how it is done. Attitude, body language and tone of voice are so important as are the small passing comments or actions that can be anything from a pleasant, kind interaction to a cruel, barbed, hurtful episode which affects the resident long after the worker has moved on to other matters.

If asked about the quality of care or life in a particular care home, families or residents are unlikely to highlight:

- "the competent manner the nurse inserted a catheter"
- "the efficient manner that the housekeeper cleaned the sink and checked the COSHH requirements of the cleaning fluid"
- "the quality of the maintenance workers' electrical wiring".

Much more likely is that they will measure the quality of care by reflecting on the relationships they have formed and how staff respond to them as in:

- "the care staff are lovely, Jan got me a yoghurt whenever I felt peckish"
- "Peter the maintenance man always chats with me about the football and brings me the programme after the game"
- "Betty always asks me if I want my sideboard polished today".

These examples may appear petty or insignificant, but it is often the smallest things that can make the biggest difference to how a resident feels.

Some staff have little awareness of how to respond to residents. Some may feel engagement is not permitted or is not part of their role, others may not know how to respond or have enough local knowledge to be able to engage.

Kindness can be demonstrated through body language and tone of voice without the intervention taking any longer. For example, when serving a person a drink, the worker can do the same task in a variety of ways and give a number of different messages:

1. put the drink down firmly and loudly with no words or eye contact
2. put the drink down quietly with no words and avoiding eye contact
3. put the drink down quietly with smiling eyes and mouth and a few gentle words.

The same action performed differently gives so many alternative messages. Clearly the third example is ideal but what about the first two? They cannot of themselves be described as abusive since it would not be possible to make a judgement about whether the actions 'hurt the resident's feelings', made them feel a nuisance or made them feel unwanted. However, if this type of activity is allowed to develop and become entrenched it will lead to staff seeing residents simply as recipients of tasks, with consequent dehumanisation. Their approach to residents could become disrespectful or even abusive. Thus, poor routines and practices become institutionalised and the risk of organisational abuse is heightened.

Treating staff with kindness and compassion

The impact of the organisation on staff morale must not be dismissed nor the impact of the culture of the organisation on how staff treat each other and residents. Caring for each other as a team across all roles in the organisation will support positive attitudes to each other, as well as to residents and relatives. Dewar (2011 & 2013) gives examples of how the leader can show compassion towards staff. These include:

- remembering the names of new staff rather than using terms such as the cleaner or the admin assistant
- giving positive specific feedback about the contribution the worker makes to the home
- noticing if others are not feeling their best and working together to help them
- taking account of other perspectives rather than insisting the leader is always right.

Challenging barriers to kindness and compassion

Care homes are governed by so many laws, rules and regulations that it has become easy to believe that we have reached a stage where the residents can be denied everything which requires a little extra care and thought. However practical care and compassion can take many forms. This might include:

- enabling a resident to keep their dog and organising a staff rota to feed and walk it
- working with a resident to plan a meal for a special celebration
- buying some adapted gardening equipment so that a resident can help the gardener
- buying a small mobile oven so that residents can do baking in the dining room.

The most common reason given in residential care for preventing residents participating in an activity is that 'health and safety' won't allow it. Although this may be an issue on some occasions, there are still plenty of opportunities for many activities provided that risk assessments are carried out and appropriate measures put in place to keep residents safe. Health and safety legislation requires risks to be appropriately managed which is not the same as requiring activities to be banned. Leaders with a 'can do' approach develop a positive culture and encourage staff about how much can be achieved.

Supporting staff to know about local culture and idioms

Many overseas staff make a crucial contribution to the care of residents in the UK. However, the challenge of communicating in another language has been identified as a barrier to care (Georgiou 2014 and Lupton & Croft-White 2013). Another difficulty for overseas staff is their lack of knowledge of local culture and social customs. It is a difficulty which must be addressed by the leader to ensure that it does not impact on residents' wellbeing. It can be hard to identify and teach local customs and culture – sometimes even harder for those who have been born and brought up there because they know no other way – but it is an important challenge worth taking up. Common local words should also be identified. In Sussex, for example, a narrow footpath is a 'twitten' while in Derbyshire a bread roll is referred to as a 'cob'.

National customs and etiquette such as always saying 'please' and 'thank you', 'excuse me' and 'sorry' if you bump into someone else, holding doors open for others and forming orderly queues are all British customs that may not be known to overseas staff. If staff inadvertently do not do or say these things, residents could consider them rude and difficulties in the relationship develop.

EXAMPLE

Mary was an elderly lady who was particularly tearful one Sunday – Mothering Sunday - when she saw other residents being visited by their children. The carer asked her what was wrong but she could not understand what Mary was talking about. Mary tried explaining that she had lost her only child to cancer two years earlier and that day was Mothering Sunday, but the carer was Chinese and had no knowledge of the UK significance of the date or the traditions of the day.

It is important for overseas staff to have some knowledge of both national and local history, for example the local industries that might influence the medical conditions of some residents. Without knowing about local disasters and events it is harder for staff to have compassionate or appropriate conversations. Understanding how local people normally live can help staff understand their residents and relatives better.

Using the head, the heart and the hands

For staff, in whatever role they have, to support residents successfully requires a combination of knowledge, skills and compassion often described as involving:

- the head – the knowledge to know how to do the task
- the hands – the ability to physically undertake the task
- the heart – the desire to do the task with kindness, compassion, humanity and, if appropriate, laughter.

Managing professional boundaries and giving of oneself

There can be difficulties for a leader who is keen to encourage staff to give something of themselves but at the same time not cross professional boundaries. The more inclusive and 'family focused' the culture of care is, for example, the greater the risk of staff crossing boundaries. How familiar can staff become with residents and relatives, or how informal can conversations become? There are no clear guidelines or rules about these matters, but some activities, as set out below, can be seen in general terms as being beneficial to residents' wellbeing although there will always be exceptions. Staff might choose to:

- bring in their own pets
- encourage their children to visit and talk to the residents
- bring their families to care home functions
- tell residents about their holidays or what their children are doing at school
- have a bit of light-hearted conversation about sport, local issues or some aspect of life in the home
- have light-hearted 'cheeky' conversations.

However, staff should also have clear boundaries and not discuss:

- personal problems
- personal finances
- issues concerning other residents
- issues concerning other staff, the management of the care home or their working conditions.

How can kindness and compassion be measured?

As suggested earlier, research continues to struggle with a precise definition of compassion. Arguably, if it cannot be defined, it remains a largely unquantifiable and immeasurable phenomenon (Schulz in Perry 2009). But simply saying that it is either 'present' or 'absent' is not helpful without quantifying what is present or absent. Beth Perry (2009) undertook a small research study where she describes the small things that make a difference in a person's life as "attending to the essential ordinary". She showed that what is often of greatest value to a resident are the small things that go unnoticed until they no longer happen and only then is their full value understood.

The challenge of trying to capture care and compassion was put to the author of this book in 2010 by the Chief Nurse of Brighton Hospital Trust, when she was trying to find a way of measuring when the trust staff demonstrated care and compassion.

A simple observation tool called Sit & See™ was developed. It captures and records the smallest things that make the biggest difference to patient care. The tool describes positive, passive and poor care in 14 fundamental areas of care. It does not seek to measure *what* was undertaken but *how* it was undertaken.

The observer can sit for 15-50 minutes and observe and celebrate tiny examples of care and compassion. For example a smile, a little banter, a reassuring touch or perhaps sorting out a resident's radio can make all the difference. Sometimes it may be necessary for the observer to show how to improve aspects of care. After just 2.5 hours training, an observer will learn to recognise tiny examples of care or compassion and, using a simple recording system, can identify positive, passive or poor care.

Staff using the tool see care through the resident's eyes which gives them an understanding of the difference even the smallest interactions can make to how the patient feels. They also learn how to reflect and discuss care and compassion and the challenges of delivering compassionate care, as well as no longer being prepared to excuse dispassionate care.

The different types of care and compassion

- **Positive care and compassion:** Staff show they respect their residents and visitors. They use every opportunity to engage with and/or solve difficulties without giving the impression that the task is either too much trouble or not their responsibility. The resident is treated first and foremost as a person and their medical condition is treated as secondary to the needs of the person as a fellow human being.
- **Passive care and compassion:** Staff attend to the residents and visitors but are business-like and impartial, showing no obvious emotion or visual signs of caring or respecting the resident as a person. However residents are *not* treated simply as an object or medical condition.
- **Poor care and compassion:** Staff either fail to attend to residents and visitors or attend to them abruptly using both negative tone and body language. They may not talk at all or may talk over the resident. The residents appear to be treated as objects or medical conditions.

The tool is recognised as an example of good practice by the Department of Health in the Government response to the Francis Inquiry (DH 2013) and is used in a variety of care settings. (www.sitandsee.co.uk)

POINTERS FOR PREVENTION OF ABUSE

1 **Primary prevention**
General activities, for example...

Encourage light hearted, appropriate conversation between all staff and residents.

2 **Secondary prevention**
Specific activities, for example...

Within reviews and appraisals include a section on attitudes to care and compassion, perhaps by setting possible scenarios within a care home and testing for appropriate responses.

3 **Tertiary prevention**
A response to an actual situation, for example...

Review the amount of care and compassion shown when undertaking an enquiry into a concern or complaint. If it is not immediately obvious, there may be value in using an observational tool to measure care and compassion in practice.

Chapter 6
Staff and volunteer selection: get smarter and be safe

Successful staff recruitment is a central part of excellent provision of care for older people and significantly reduces the chances of resident abuse occurring. It can, however, be fraught with problems, be expensive and time-consuming and, for many, feel like a 'lucky dip'. Even when the most robust recruitment processes are followed the appointment can go badly wrong. It is not an exact science and has a great deal of subjectivity about it. However, there are systems and processes that can be followed to reduce the risk of a failed appointment.

1.3 million people work in social care, the majority of whom are unregistered care staff. Turnover in some care homes is high, causing instability in the home and an increased risk of abusive practice as continuity of care becomes compromised. Agency staff may be used to reinforce permanent staff but they do bring their own challenges. Agency staff will not know the residents, the building, or the organisation's policy and procedures. Because they do not know the residents they may not be able to be proactive or anticipate a resident's needs. They can cause permanent staff to become disgruntled that the agency staff have less responsibility yet earn more. For the leader the anxiety caused by the increased risks of a home being run by agency staff should not be underestimated.

On the other hand, agency staff are invaluable at times of crisis. When extra staff are needed to offer one-to-one care it is important to give clear information about the person being cared for, including their interests and the reason for, and purpose of, the one-to-one care. Some homes have an internal 'bank' of temporary or 'zero hours' contract staff. Their advantage is that these staff know the home, will be familiar with policies and procedures and may know the resident from previous shifts.

It is important but easily forgotten that bank staff should be given the opportunity to participate in mandatory training, supervision and development work to ensure they understand and practise the culture of care required by the home.

Filling staff vacancies may not be easy for a variety of reasons, of which low pay is only one. The location of the home can influence the availability of staff. The obvious obstacle for a home in a small town or rural area is poor transport links. There may, also, be competition from other work opportunities in the area that attract a similar pay scale. In the case of Orchid View, the home was close to Gatwick Airport which made the problems of recruitment worse.

Senior managers and company owners should ensure there is in place a workforce development strategy or plan regarding the recruitment, support and development of staff able to deliver the care as required. They must also be able to evidence they can deliver the plan (Georgiou 2014).

It can be difficult for leaders without direct influence on strategic workforce planning, but to safeguard residents and demonstrate due diligence they must be prepared to place any staffing concerns they may have on record and ensure senior personnel are aware of their concerns.

Filling a vacancy

The focus when filling a vacancy must be to find the most suitable person for the role. This may sound obvious but, when considering recruitment in the context of prevention of abuse, the process could easily become, instead, recruitment of a person who represents the least possible risk, even if they do not have much aptitude for the work!

Before advertising to fill a vacant post it is important to be clear what sort of person is required for the role, when the post needs to be filled and how much the salary will be. If the post is a new development, this forethought will already have been undertaken, but if it is to fill an existing vacancy it is easy and natural to simply think that the post should be filled in the same way as it was before. In care this may be the most appropriate action – however, it can be helpful to pause and consider whether the vacancy could be the opportunity to resolve difficulties or implement a new initiative by using the money from the vacancy in a different way.

A vacancy is also an ideal time to consider whether the grade of the position is appropriate for the activity that is required. This review could result in the post requiring an upgrade and so more financial resources being required. But it may also result in redefining the role and introducing a post that can support the residents in a different way.

Line management and developing teams

Homes that have weak leadership are more at risk of organisational abuse. Weak leadership is not necessarily having a leader or manager who lacks either lustre or direction. It may simply be that they have been promoted above their level of competence and are unable to carry out the work. It could also be that the leader is competent but there is no structure of supervision in place to support the manager in upholding standards.

A career structure for supporting staff both in direct and indirect care improves assurance in the home, improves supervision and support for new staff and gives autonomy and responsibility to workers who are able to enhance the culture of care. So when a leader is thinking about how to fill a vacancy, the post's career structure and extent of supervision should be carefully considered.

Safer staff recruitment

Once the type of job has been identified, a job description and advertisement should be prepared. The requirements of the post need to be set out alongside terms and conditions. There should also be a short but accurate description of the expectations regarding positive practice and adult safeguarding, particularly with respect to prevention of abuse and resident empowerment. Safer recruitment guidance also recommends that organisations taking successful staff through the induction process practise continual vigilance within a safe culture (Buckinghamshire 2013).

The post should be advertised internally and to external candidates. However tempting it may be to short-circuit the recruitment process because the 'ideal' candidate already works for the organisation, the application for a new role is an ideal opportunity to revisit the candidate's personal values and their understanding of the organisation's culture of care and approach to adult safeguarding, regardless of how long they have worked in the organisation already.

Recruitment policy

The organisation should have a written recruitment policy which links with the adult safeguarding policy, and highlights the aspects of the recruitment procedure that have been put in place as part of the safeguarding process. The leader co-ordinating the recruitment process should be able to comply with safeguarding policy while feeling confident that they are doing all they can to find the best person to fill the vacancy. Any advertisement should highlight the nature of the work with vulnerable adults and confirm that a criminal record check, relevant to the country of recruitment, will be undertaken.

The application form

The extent of application forms varies widely from organisation to organisation. They should be appropriate to the role that is being advertised and information should only be requested if it can help in the safe recruitment process. A successful application form requests essential information but also important information which is less obvious. For example:

- **Previous names and date of birth** – Has the person worked for the organisation in the past? Why did they leave? Are there any reasons for concern and have they mentioned it elsewhere?
- **National Insurance number and work permits** – It is vital to establish if the person has a right to work in the UK. This right may need to be supported by a work permit or a work visa. The validity of this number should be checked if possible to ensure it relates to the person named in the application. Even homes that have a thorough recruitment process have been 'caught out' by workers falsifying or obtaining a National Insurance number and trying to work even though they are in the UK illegally. If the home can demonstrate they have taken all reasonable actions to ensure the worker is in the UK legally the home will not be prosecuted. This contrasts with homes that are exposed as employing illegal immigrants to provide care, such as a home in Hampshire which was investigated for concerns about care (www.telegraph.co.uk, 31 July 2010). In 2008 a leaked government report found that hundreds of illegal immigrants have found work in British care homes. The report, based on information obtained during 2006, showed the use of illegal immigrants was widespread and significant (www.theguardian.com, 30 March 2008). Employing overseas workers who do not have a permit to work puts residents at risk. It will also attract large fines for the organisation from the UK Border Agency and could result in prosecution or professional misconduct charges being taken against the leader who employs them (www.derbytelegraph.co.uk, 17 November 2013).
- **A full employment history** – This should be reviewed and the applicant asked to explain any gaps. The history might also show repeated job changes without any clear career or salary progression that should be thoroughly scrutinised at interview.
- **Referees** – Two referees, including one from the candidate's most recent post working with vulnerable groups, are required. The referees should not be family members or close friends of the applicant. They should be sent a set form and job description to enable them to give information relevant to the post. Read the reference carefully to establish not only what has been written but also if there are any phrases that might be vague or used to 'gloss over' an issue. The referee should be contacted if clarification is required.

Assessing one candidate against another

Assessing candidates is best achieved using a grid identifying the qualities that are required for the role, including qualifications and experience. Each candidate's qualifications should be reviewed for relevance to the post and whether they have skills that are truly transferable. Perhaps the person has a qualification or skill that is not directly relevant but there are components that mean the person may be very well suited to the post. Conversely the person may have a qualification that appears ideal, for example being a registered nurse, but only on closer questioning does it emerge that they have mainly worked as a paediatric nurse or in ITU – work which does not equip them ideally to work in a care home with older people. Filling a vacant nursing post with any registered nurse simply because they have the required qualification could be a dangerous and short-sighted decision.

Involving residents and family members in the interview process

The best judge of whether a person is suitable to work in a care home is often the resident and/or family member. Using residents or their families as part of the recruitment panel needs to be managed and can be done in a number of ways:

- residents can be introduced to candidates in the lounge and invited to have a general chat; and their informal views obtained afterwards
- arrange for a resident or family member(s) to meet the candidates and show them around before the interview, again gathering their opinions after the interviews
- it may be possible to support residents to be active members of the interview panel. Preparation of the residents is important. In particular it is important they understand legal parameters about the nature of questions that can be asked, for example ensuring they understand it is not possible to ask a woman if she is going to start a family, or make any reference to sexual orientation or the candidate's appearance. They should not be shown the application form or references. There should be a discussion beforehand about the questions that are going to be asked, and each resident encouraged to focus on one aspect of the role being applied for. After the interview residents may need support to complete the scoring system for which time must be built into the interview timetable.

The interview

The aim of the interview is to establish some facts about the candidate and explore their values, attitudes and motivation to work with older people and their emotional maturity. Core questions will help structure the process, using open-ended questions that enable the candidate to describe examples of practice or knowledge. Their body language, tone of voice and approach to the residents they meet will all be good indicators of their suitability for the post.

The interview is also an important time to introduce the candidate to the organisation's approach to safeguarding, its culture of care and approach to residents and relatives. Remember that those candidates with limited knowledge of care, or who have worked for organisations where safeguarding only focuses on reporting and investigation, may not be able to articulate the subtleties of the resilience model of safeguarding. Their response should be viewed in the context of their overall attitude and their understanding of how residents can be harmed by staff in a care setting.

EXAMPLE

A woman applied for a role as a care assistant. She presented at interview with body piercing, tattoos and one side of her head shaved. One reference detailed her poor timekeeping and high sickness record. She was interviewed by the care leader and a resident who, on first impression, felt very negative and did not think she would be suitable. However, the interview process allowed the applicant to demonstrate her compassion, positive attitude and enthusiasm for work with older people. This allowed the leader and resident to overcome their initial reservations. She was questioned about her timekeeping and a third reference was obtained which was positive. The woman was offered the role and proved herself to be a valuable member of the team.

Reviewing the criminal record

If a candidate is successful, their criminal record must be obtained and considered. If there are convictions careful consideration must be given to whether they:

- are relevant to the post applied for
- indicate that the candidate poses a risk to vulnerable adults.

Some leaders may take the view that any conviction indicates that the candidate is unsuitable to work in a care home. This approach is short-sighted and may not be acting in the best interests of the home. Any convictions should be risk assessed and considered carefully. It may be appropriate to ask the candidate to come back to discuss the disclosure information, if this was not done at the interview. The risk assessment should include:

- the nature of the conviction
- the age of the conviction
- the relevance of the conviction to the role
- details of any rehabilitation that has occurred since the conviction
- whether the candidate was in a position of trust.

Criminal records may not be available for overseas candidates and leaders should be mindful that the non-availability of information does not either automatically include or preclude the candidate from the post.

Checking professional registration

All professional registrations should be checked with the appropriate professional bodies. The most common professional registration in a care home is for registered nurse. It is vital that the status of every registration is checked with the Nursing and Midwifery Council (NMC). A nurse may not be registered for four reasons:

- they have allowed their registration to lapse by not paying the registration fee
- they have completed their nurse training or adaptation course but the registration process has not been completed
- they have been removed from the register following a fitness-to-practice hearing
- their registration is suspended by the NMC as a fitness-to-practice investigation is being undertaken.

Whatever the reason, if a nurse is not registered it is unlawful for them to practice as a registered nurse, and the care leader cannot use them in this role.

Induction

Appointing the ideal new recruit is only the first stage in developing them into a valuable and positive member of the team who will uphold the organisation's culture of care.

All staff are required to have induction and fundamental training but the manner of this training and its quality varies enormously (Cavendish 2013). All induction programmes should have a golden thread of safeguarding and person-centred care running through them, whatever the subject is. Programmes run by external trainers should be commissioned only if they reinforce the positive safeguarding model of practice.

The new recruit should be required to complete a questionnaire after they have finished the induction to ensure they have fully embedded the training. This questionnaire can also be used to provide useful feedback on the induction process.

The presence of new recruits can also provide a good test bed to discover if the skills, values and culture learned in induction are being used in practice, or if they are being thwarted by the negative practices and attitudes of existing staff. A good indicator of an organisationally abusive environment can be that staff are not undertaking care in the way they were taught, and they have set their own rules and attitudes towards residents (BBC *Panorama* 2014).

Supporting overseas staff

Many workers providing care and support to older people are overseas staff, often with English as a second language. It is important that all staff are able to speak, understand and read and write in English in order for them to understand the role they have to fulfil and to be able to record any interventions they make. Older people may find a staff member's broken English or broad accent difficult to understand which may make it difficult for her/him to build a relationship with the resident. Language difficulties may also mean the staff member cannot meet the residents' needs as well as they should because:

- they do not understand policies, procedures and care plans
- they cannot communicate effectively with other professionals, team members or families
- they cannot understand what is being asked of them
- they cannot understand the emotions being expressed by a resident.

If necessary, English language tests should be carried out to protect the residents. The individual cultural and religious beliefs of all residents should be respected and upheld by all staff within the home. While there have been recent improvements in ensuring residents from ethnic minorities have their faith and cultural needs met, there is little evidence, unfortunately, to suggest there have been successful initiatives to explain the culture and beliefs of the local population to overseas staff. This failure has the direct potential of denying cultural support to the residents who are indigenous to the location because the home has failed to ensure their overseas staff have received any education about, or familiarisation with, the local (and national) customs and social history that could be important to these residents. In the organisational abuse of residents at Orchid View the lack of support for overseas staff to ensure their language and cultural awareness was satisfactory was identified as an issue requiring a specific recommendation in the Serious Case Review (Georgiou 2014).

Volunteers

Volunteers and the friends of a care home should be subject to a formal recruitment process. It does not need to be as onerous as for paid staff, but should establish the applicants':

- reasons for wanting to be involved
- level of commitment they are able to offer
- ability to provide references.

A criminal record check should always be undertaken. If all of these checks are carried out in a spirit of positive safeguarding, volunteers will be supportive of the approach.

POINTERS FOR PREVENTION OF ABUSE

1 Primary prevention
General activities, for example…

It is important there is a clear and open policy that the home always follows the same recruitment procedures, even for internal positions.

2 Secondary prevention
Specific activities, for example…

Involve residents or relatives in the interviewing process and identify what it is they would like to know about the candidates to ensure they feel safe.

3 Tertiary prevention
A response to an actual situation, for example…

At interview, examine all job applications in detail, and if questions remain unanswered or there is any doubt about suitability, have the courage not to appoint.

Chapter 7
Effective leadership to reduce the risk of organisational abuse

The only constant in life is that nothing will stay the same forever. This applies as much to the care environment as it does to one's private life.

The most valuable resource a leader has in the care home is the staff. It is vital they feel part of the home and are involved in decision making about how to implement new or different approaches. The reality is that however good the leader is and however close to the team they feel, they must always be mindful that innovation and new developments can be disruptive and threatening to some staff because it upsets the status quo and requires staff to think and act differently. So staff must be involved right from the start and in all changes. Changes may be large or small and may refer to how an individual resident is supported or cared for. The change of approach may seem perfectly logical to the leader, but may be resisted by some staff for a multitude of reasons.

Conversely it might be that an idea or approach is put forward and the majority of the team think it is a good idea but one person thinks, for good reasons, the idea is unwise but feels unable to say anything because they might appear silly. The reality, however, might be that the majority of the group have not really thought things through and are simply following the herd. This behaviour is referred to as 'group think', just one of the obstacles a leader might come across when trying to ensure that residents are well cared for and not abused.

The danger of weak leadership
Weak leadership has been identified as a key component in organisational abuse of older people (Lupton & Croft-White 2013, Georgiou 2014). This is leadership where the person in charge is not clear about their own responsibilities or those of others. It may include:

- being distracted away from care by becoming focused on financial matters
- lack of skills and expertise to lead a team
- lack of personality or authority to stand up to lacklustre or dangerous practices or to ensure care is assessed, carried out and recorded in an appropriate manner.

There are a variety of different leadership styles and different approaches which may need to be used at different times. The three most commonly described styles are:

- **Autocratic leadership** – the leader makes all the decisions and tells staff what should happen. Staff are not allowed to be involved in the decision-making process and are actively dissuaded from passing on an opinion or giving a suggestion.
- **Democratic leadership** – describes a leader who seeks the views of staff and leads by consensus, trying to involve everybody and understand everyone's perspective.
- **Laisser-faire leadership** – describes a leader who 'goes with the flow', believing that staff will do the right thing for the right reasons. Such a leader either does not feel the need, or does not have the confidence, to take decisions themselves, and so the team is led instead by the strongest personalities in the team.

In reality an effective leader will be a combination of all of these types.

A healthy working environment will encourage individual staff members to blossom, make their own decisions and develop the skills to act autonomously, but it is vital that they know the parameters of their role and they have clear guidance from their leader about the areas of their work when they can or cannot act independently.

A successful leader will ensure staff are involved in discussing and working out how to develop new practices, implement new directives (perhaps a National Requirement), or explore alternative ways of supporting a resident. However the leader must have the skill to balance the discussion, debate and possible dissent and how long it can be allowed to run before the leader takes steps to make the best decision. The leader must not allow objections or 'sabotage' of a new initiative by staff to hamper the development of a positive culture of care simply because staff do not want a change in their working life.

A similar approach applies to staff who procrastinate or are reluctant to implement a particular approach to care. The leader may initially take the approach of gentle reminders when they see staff not carrying out care correctly or as agreed; but the leader must also set clear parameters to indicate the level of tolerance for the delay in carrying out a new approach. An ineffective leader will find it difficult or impossible to set the required boundaries and then, if necessary, deal with a non-compliant staff member by establishing their reasons for non-compliance and enforcing a change in behaviour or managing the behaviour through disciplinary procedures.

A successful leader will be able to demonstrate an ability to manage the change or development that needs to be done, listening to staff concerns and identifying the reasons for any expressed objections to change.

Care home cultures and the obstacles to upholding safe care

The leader who is working to ensure the home has safe positive practices and procedures in place to safeguard residents needs to consider the possible power base(s) that may be fuelling dissent or resistance to change. Each type of organisational culture has a different focus of power which will influence how successful or destructive a culture can be:

- **The team culture** within any care home will vary greatly. Its inner culture will have unwritten rules and basic assumptions, attitudes and prejudices. Organisational culture was researched in the 1980s by Charles Handy who identified four different types of culture. There is not necessarily one 'right' culture because different behaviours and approaches are required in different situations. If the leader understands that there are cultures within cultures it is easier to understand where some obstacles to safe resident care may be occurring.

- **The power culture** is characterised by a strong charismatic person who is the central leader. This can be positive and helpful when speedy decisions are required, but it may be that the person fulfilling this role is not in an appropriate position of authority to make the decisions they are making.

- **The role culture** describes a culture in which a team or set of individuals are efficient when life is predictable. Innovations, however, are only accepted up to a point and permitted to work alongside entrenched practice and not instead of it. Individuals work to the direction of another but do not easily cope with change.

- **The task culture** describes an environment in which the team bases its performance on results. It can be a creative culture, and one which relies on expertise and not simply on positional authority. If there is a positive environment the team will flourish as they thrive on seeing their work benefiting the results or outcomes.

- **The person culture** describes a team that is in reality a group of individuals who happen to work together. The philosophy is that the organisation is there to help the individual and management is a chore. The strength of individuals and personalities determines the approach of the rest of the team. Individuals are listened to not because of their knowledge and experience, but because of their persuasive nature. Myths and rituals can be built up around the idiosyncrasies of these individuals as people believe them without question (Hamson *et al* 1992 in Phair & Good 1998).

The power of leadership

A strong leader does not simply dictate to staff what should be done. A strong leader influences the staff so that they do what is needed to safeguard residents. The influence of a leader is often referred to as power and leaders have different types of power available to them to use at different times so they can make the changes they want or ensure the required care is carried out. There are five types of power that are commonly recognised and used by a leader. Most, if not all, will play a part in ensuring the safe care of residents, providing the leader uses the right type of power at the right time and for the right reasons:

- **Reward power** – describes how the leader is able to offer a reward to the staff for successfully completing a task or behaving in a certain way. The reward needs to appeal to the staff and be relevant and not demeaning. They must believe the leader will give the reward as promised if the goal is achieved. Any reward should be proportionate to the task and should not be used simply to encourage staff to complete work that is considered part of their core duties. The reward may be subtle or emotional in nature, for example the feeling of satisfaction or pleasure in seeing residents enjoying a new development. Alternatively the reward may be acknowledgement in a staff bulletin or at the organisation's awards ceremony.
- **Coercive power** – is based on the leader having control over what happens to staff if they do not act as required. This power should be used appropriately but should be considered as the 'bottom line'. Staff should clearly understand that the leader will not allow individuals to engage in organisationally abusive practices simply because staff do not want to change or work in accordance with best practice or within the organisation's culture, particularly its approach to residents.
- **Legitimate power** – describes the type of power that staff believe a leader has to instruct them and to expect them to follow instructions. This power may come simply from a leader's job title (such as manager, senior carer, or area manager) which in itself suggests that it gives the leader the right to give orders. Confusion can arise when a leader in one department, for example an administration manager, believes they have the right to instruct care staff to carry out certain duties and the care staff automatically assume they must obey simply because of the job title.
- **Referent power** – describes the type of power that a leader possesses when staff follow them because they are admired by others. Referent power is personality and charisma driven. It can be a positive force for change if a key person with referent power in the team is working positively with the leader to ensure positive practice is upheld. Equally it can be a negative influence if the person with referent power is using their influence to resist change or developments or is undermining the legitimate leader's position through their own powerful personality.
- **Expert power** – describes how staff will follow a person because they have expert knowledge or skills that are relevant to the job. The person who has expert power might not have overall legitimate power, but could be the key positive influence on a development or the key antagonist if their expertise has not been taken into account.

The dangers of 'group think'

Group think, referred to earlier in this chapter, is a subtle but real phenomenon that can easily take over decision-making processes or investigations into incidents. In essence group think is a term that refers to a psychological phenomenon in which people strive for consensus within a group (Janis 1977). People opt to set aside their own opinions and remain quiet, preferring to keep the peace rather than disrupt the uniformity of the crowd. Janis (1977) suggested it may occur when people believe their ideas or opinions will be rejected. Effectively they do not want to look foolish or appear to be obstructive or difficult. It is thought to occur when the group members have a lot in common, are perhaps from the same staff group, and where there is a powerful and charismatic leader who dominates the group. Difficulties for individuals in expressing their opinion can be increased when the group is placed under extreme stress or a moral dilemma exists.

The term 'group' does not necessarily describe a collection of people brought together to make specific decisions, but could also refer to a specific team or, indeed, an entire organisation. There are seven main symptoms of group think identified by Janis and Mann (1977) which can relate to the team in a care home, or an organisation faced with examining care practices that have been exposed as of concern and may need improvement:

1. the group ignores obvious signs of concern and is overly optimistic about the ease with which matters can be put right
2. the group discredits those who have raised concerns, or too easily explain concerns away
3. the group believes what it is doing is morally correct and does not consider the wider ethical consequences of its decision(s)
4. the group has negative stereotypes of rivals outside the group who it considers may be a threat (often incorrectly)
5. members of the group who disagree with the opinions or actions of the group as a whole are labelled as disloyal
6. members of the group falsely perceive that everyone agrees with the group's decision and silence is seen as consent
7. some group members self-select for themselves the role of protecting the group from adverse information.

If these seven characteristics are considered in the context of the findings of the *Serious Case Review of Orchid View* (Georgiou 2014), group think was evident both within the team at the care home and by senior managers within the organisation. Over a period of 18 months the home had six managers but only one was registered. A series of safeguarding concerns were raised by families as well as by statutory services, yet nothing in the home changed. Residents continued to suffer weight loss, dehydration, medication administration errors, poor staffing levels and staff sleeping while on duty. The Care Quality Commission undertook inspections as well as the community pharmacist, and still nothing changed. A large-scale investigation only commenced after a whistleblower, who was the home administration manager, went to the police.

After the large-scale safeguarding investigation was initiated, senior managers assured the safeguarding team that quality managers were concentrating on quality control and made a number of assurances including giving assurances that they would tell families about the safeguarding concerns, yet they did not. The ongoing response by management continued to be inadequate. The worrying emerging themes were not identified or examined with the required honesty and objectivity. Residents and relatives were not informed about the safeguarding concerns. Similarly, staff told the coroner at the inquest into the deaths of 19 people that they were not informed about safeguarding concerns either, and did not understand what was happening, increasing their anxiety and suspicions about the incoming safeguarding service.

How a leader can avoid group think

The theory of how to avoid group think is described in five simple statements by Janis and Mann (1977):

- the group should be made aware of the causes and consequences of group think
- the leader should be neutral initially withholding all opinions and expectations, and should encourage an atmosphere of open enquiry
- the leader should give high priority to airing objections and doubts and readily accept criticism
- groups should always consider unpopular alternatives, embracing the role of devil's advocate if appropriate
- it may be helpful to divide the group into separate bodies to enable all options to be considered.

The challenge for a leader is how to translate these theoretical actions into practice, particularly if there are groups or individuals trying to undermine the leader, using the principles of group think against the leader.

In any situation a leader is limited by only being able to act within their own sphere of influence and in line with their own professional, ethical and moral duties and beliefs. For example, the managers at Orchid View were certainly ineffective but they could not force senior managers to examine the concerns more rigorously in 2010 or 2011. Therefore a leader must focus on what they do have control over, however large or small that focus of control is, and can help to avoid group think occurring in their care home by applying some practical principles:

- Always listen to the voice of residents and families openly.
- Seek the view and opinions of even the most meek staff member.
- Try and view external agencies who inspect and regulate as professionals who have the same focus on 'the wellbeing of the resident'.
- Ask 'why' about everything you do not understand and 'how' about the delivery of care. And keep asking until the answers are found.
- Support the team to consider concerns from the resident's perspective. Whatever reasons are used to justify an action, reflect on whether they really make it 'ok' for the resident.
- Develop a sense of connectedness between staff, residents and relatives that encourages as many opportunities of shared care, improved openness and understanding as possible (Lupton & Croft-White 2013).
- By being open, honest and prepared to learn from the past, the leader will be supporting the provision of a resilient care environment which is able to adapt. A learning organisation is one in which a leader supports staff to think about and honestly analyse why mistakes occurred, to learn from mistakes (and don't forget near misses), and so be in a position to anticipate and avoid risks and situations where harm could occur in the future.
- The leader should be ever mindful that the organisation's culture is not fixed and will be constantly evolving. A good and high quality care home can experience a shift from good to poor care very quickly, within a matter of months, perhaps because external factors are combining with internal triggers. A leader must be ever conscious of these possibilities and of the signs that suggest a care home is beginning to fail (Lupton & Croft-White 2013).
- Know the team and identify key staff members and how they influence others. Work with them and their strengths to engage together in upholding the standards and culture within the home which you want.

EXAMPLE

A senior care worker had been employed for 12 years in the same care home. She had a reputation for being efficient and getting 'the work done'. A member of staff began to realise that one particular resident was often quickly got up in the morning, ready for breakfast, even when other staff were busy. The care worker was curious because the resident needed to be transferred with a hoist, which required two staff. What she saw was the senior care worker using the hoist alone, placing the resident in great danger. When challenged by the care assistant the senior told her not to tell anyone. The care worker felt she had to fulfil her responsibility to the resident and reported the matter to the care home leader who, after following correct disciplinary procedures, terminated the senior care worker's employment.

POINTERS FOR PREVENTION OF ABUSE

1 Primary prevention
General activities, for example...

Hold routine staff meetings, and give reasons for any decisions which have to be made that are resident focussed. Ask staff to offer ideas for other solutions.

2 Secondary prevention
Specific activities, for example...

If there is a particularly difficult problem, set up a multi-disciplinary staff group or quality circle with staff made up of different grades to find a solution. Make the focus the needs of the resident and not those of the staff.

3 Tertiary prevention
A response to an actual situation, for example...

If a staff member refuses to implement a new approach or improve their attitude, examine what power they might have in the home alongside any reasons they give for their dissent. If residents are at risk from the staff member's actions or attitude, have the courage to deal with the situation decisively and those who may be influenced by the team member.

Chapter 8
How relatives and residents can trust the care home

Families of care home residents can play an important role in preventing abuse; but this does not happen naturally or automatically. Failure to engage with, listen to and work with families not only fails the resident at that moment, but can possibly mean that the home leader has failed to hear, see, understand and investigate more widespread concerns. It may not always be easy to work with a family: they may find the fact that they do not have an automatic right to decide what should happen with their loved one difficult to accept. On occasion the family may also cause the vulnerable resident such distress that the home has to seek recourse through the courts to protect them. These situations are, however, rare. The vast majority of families simply want their relative to be well cared for and have a quality of life that gives them pleasure and enjoyment.

A significant lesson to be leant from Orchid View (Georgiou 2014), was that families were not welcomed and they were not involved in the life, or decision making, of their relatives. Nor were they listened to despite witnessing resident suffering and the home failing. Families and society will remain anxious and concerned about their relatives being admitted to care homes while scandals continue to be exposed both by the media and investigations such as that at Orchid View.

Good safeguarding practice requires the staff, manager and organisation to build relationships with relatives so there is trust. Relatives do not necessarily believe that everything will always be perfect and there will never be problems. Care is a human activity provided by error-prone humans for humans. However, the crucial factor for relatives is what is being done to try and prevent things going wrong and what is done when errors occur, both immediately and in the longer term. Families also want to know that they are being listened to and that their concerns are taken seriously.

For relatives at Orchid View, for example, there was evidence that they were misled regarding the competence of staff, and were not told about any of the safeguarding concerns that were being investigated despite the organisation having agreed to write to them. The relatives' representatives asked the *Serious*

Case Review author (Georgiou 2014) many questions which were finally synthesised into four questions:

- How can the public be confident that:
    - the organisations they entrust the care of their loved ones to are properly managed, with good governance and financial security?
    - the organisations provide the good quality of care that they advertise and receive payment for, from private individuals or the public purse?
- How can people be confident that they or their relative will be safe and well cared for?
- What support is available to residents and their relatives, and how do they know about it and how to use it, if there are concerns about the service?
- How can organisations and individual professionals be accountable for the safety, quality and practice in their services?

Leaders need to think about these questions with regard to their own practice to ensure the chances of a disconnection between them and relatives are greatly reduced.

The legal rights of the family

Families play an important and often pivotal role in the lives of a resident, usually with the best intentions and the full consent of the resident. However, the care leader has a legal duty to ensure their level of involvement in decision making and care is either agreed by the resident or, if they lack capacity, is considered to be in the resident's best interest in accordance with the legislation. Some families struggle with the concepts that:

- an older person is still able to make their own decisions
- should their relative lack capacity, they cannot demand or dictate what should happen unless a legal directive which gives the family powers has been signed before the person became incapacitated.

Equally, care professionals must always be mindful that acting in a person's best interests means exactly that. The risks and benefits of any action must be considered and justification provided for any decision. Whenever possible, there should be discussion with the family members before any change in care is delivered.

Involving families in care decisions

Families understandably often feel a great sense of responsibility towards their relative. If they have previously been the carer at home, they might feel guilty that the person now needs 24-hour care in a care home. Careless language used by health and social care professionals that the family 'could no longer cope' can add to that sense of guilt and feeling of failure. Leaders can counter this negative language at every opportunity by explaining to the family that their relative's 24-hour needs became too great for one person (or a family) to manage.

Before admission, giving the family plenty of time to explain the new resident's care needs from their perspective will help to build confidence. Some families provide a summary of care needs, and proactive homes ask for relatives to provide detailed life histories and information about care needs. Staff often find it helpful to visit the new resident's own home so they get a clearer picture of them and their lives. Sometimes, however, admissions are arranged at short notice or the person is admitted from hospital, in which case the leader must ensure:

- a full and competently completed pre-admission assessment is undertaken
- they feel confident that all the person's medical conditions can be managed by the staff. If the new resident has an unusual condition, or a condition that staff have not supported for a while, it is worth arranging an urgent update or asking a key member of staff to go to the hospital to learn about the specific care needs of that condition.

The family and the resident must be able to have confidence from the start, not only in the words spoken by the leader but in the actions they take to smooth the transition from home or hospital to the care home. Leaders should ensure staff understand fully the distress a resident (and their families) may be experiencing due to the loss of their independence, especially those who may have experienced a catastrophic incident that means the person has been admitted from hospital and has had no opportunity to say 'goodbye' to their home, their possessions and their emotional attachment to their home, the community and their previous life.

EXAMPLE

Jim had spent 42 days in hospital after breaking his hip and during that period he lost three stone in weight. On arrival at his new nursing home the senior care assistant asked the family what Jim liked to eat and drink. She also set up a care plan that instructed staff to give him milky drinks, smoothies and extra treats that the family brought in. Within a week he was stronger and brighter and the family felt safe now that Jim was being cared for.

Easing the transition and working with the family and resident throughout their stay

McCormack (2003) identified five areas that need to be considered to ease transition and assure families that the resident is central to the home's activity:

- **The environment.** The environment should be one that the person finds 'healing'. This means that it helps the resident and their family feel safe and secure. The physical fabric is important but should not be used simply as a facade to project an image of good care. New buildings with modern furnishings can create a clean and bright image and some may have ornaments and soft furnishings in the corporate style. Some residents love this image but corporate soft furnishings can make a home look impersonal and more like a display in a department store than a person's home. Encourage the family to bring in personal items for their room but also for the communal areas (if appropriate). Lovely aromas, warmth, cheerful noise, spotless cleanliness as well as such nebulous phenomena as the energy of the home will help both relative and resident feel safe and at home.
- **Support.** The leader should encourage the care staff to work with the resident to grow her/his strengths and capabilities, and not simply be concerned with delivering care. Staff can gain the trust of the resident and their family by developing relationships using a key worker system which includes directly liaising with the family, and doing what they say they will do.
- **Respect.** The most effective way for staff to convince residents and relatives that they care and want to do the best they can is to show the resident respect. This can be done by helping the residents see themselves as being citizens of the home rather than simply 'residents'. This notion can be promoted by involving the residents in aspects of home life such as menu planning, care planning, helping to organise or suggest social events, and taking part in resident meetings and committees. Showing respect could also include enabling the resident to help in the home in a large or small way or activities such as becoming involved in staff selection. Some may want to oversee the decoration of their rooms, or be actively involved in the decoration of public areas or become involved in the garden, including having a small area of garden for themselves.
- **Making sense of what is happening.** Both the resident and their family will need support to adjust to the new world they find themselves in. The resident (and family) should be given time to ask questions about any aspect of the home's activities or procedures. If the family asks why something cannot be done the leader should reflect and explore carefully whether there any fundamental reasons why the request cannot be answered positively. It is these situations that set the tone of whether the leader is promoting a 'can do' philosophy which puts the residents first. Unless a negative response is supported by clear, sensible and, if necessary, legally informed answers the seeds of doubt can easily be sown about the care home's ability to care for their relative. Should the home decide to speak to the family about problems or concerns it is important the home is clear about the facts and the reasoning for any suggested change in care. Families usually accept the word of the professional, unless they have good reason to doubt it, but their later discovery of some inaccuracies in the facts presented will add to their concerns that their relative is not safe.

- **Encouraging participation.** The leader should promote the principles of autonomy and participation for all residents. Residents should not be 'done to' but should be involved in their care as much as possible, as well as the life of the home to the extent they are able or want to. Families will be reassured and have more confidence in homes that encourage engagement and which encourage staff to show an interest in the residents' families and what is happening to various family members. They will also appreciate homes that enable residents to leave the home for visits or family celebrations.

EXAMPLE

Arthur was no longer able to walk or stand and only recognised some family members intermittently. However, he was able to remember he had a great-grandson and he loved holding him and even sang to him. The family wanted him to attend his great-grandson's christening and the home willingly explored how this could be achieved. Two staff members were needed plus the home minibus. One carer stayed in the church to help Arthur's daughter push the wheelchair. Family photos were taken with Arthur and all his family. It was a special day for everyone and the last time he was well enough to leave the care home or see all his family together.

The value of residents' and relatives' meetings

Many homes offer regular residents' and relatives' meetings, but in a busy home it is something that can easily slip. The structure and purpose of the meetings can vary from purely social events with an opportunity for informal conversation to formal meetings with minutes chaired by the home manager. There is value in all types of meeting, but the most important factors are that families meet each other, and staff are prepared to listen to suggestions and concerns.

There is limited evidence about how to structure relatives' meetings so they maximise the benefits for relatives, residents and staff. Sometimes there is concern that some families may hijack the meeting simply to voice their own concerns and dominate the meeting. This is certainly a risk; however, it should be remembered that one family's single concern may be widespread and this only comes to light as families hear others expressing the same concern.

The meetings need to be held at a time that best suits the majority of families, which may be in the evening or at some point over the weekend. It is common for the manager to chair the meeting but it may be better to engage the services of a person from outside the home who has chairing skills and who has some understanding of care homes. Their independence will give confidence to families and staff that the meetings and relationships are taken seriously. The chair should ensure minutes are correct and disseminated in a timely way.

At these meetings information can be exchanged and any safeguarding concerns communicated. This may be difficult to do, but it is best that families are aware of the situation and the action that is being taken to safeguard the residents. They will be less anxious and will already be fully briefed if any information is revealed by another source.

The leader should follow up on any actions the staff have agreed to do and monitor how the staff listen and respond to comments and suggestions.

The benefits of meetings for relatives are:
- they give ongoing support and strength drawn from shared experiences with other relatives
- they offer the opportunity to express concerns and explore solutions as a group
- they build communication and relationships with staff
- they provide an educational forum about useful and relevant topics
- they give families a voice.

The benefits of meetings for residents are:
- they improve the quality of care
- they provide advocates to act on behalf of residents who are unable to give a view
- they support residents who have no family locally
- they provide a connection with the wider community
- they can plan group activities.

The benefits of meetings for staff are:
- they build three-way communication
- they provide the staff with an advisory committee for new ideas
- they help to develop relationships with residents and families provided they remain focused on resident and family needs not on staff needs
- they promote staff appreciation of each other and teamwork.

Source: www.agedcarecrisis.com/residents-rights/resident-support-groups

When things go wrong

The widespread public perception of care homes is that they offer poor care and the possibility that residents may be abused. By contrast, research supports the belief held by workers within the care sector that most experiences are positive and residents' quality of care is good (PSSRU 2011). In a study by the Personal Social Services Research Unit at the University of Kent, most residents felt their experience was more positive than they had expected. Their quality of life had improved, they were not isolated and they saw family and friends as much as, or more than, they used to. Relatives were also generally positive about their experience (PSSRU 2011).

From time to time things may go wrong, or the relative or resident may believe things should have been done differently. They may express concern that the care has not been satisfactory, or that the resident has unexplained bruises, weight loss or other causes for concern. The leader should listen and, before giving an explanation, look into the concern. Families might not want to call their concerns a complaint, but they will want to know the worries as they see them have been addressed. It may be that the perceived change in the resident's condition is an inevitable consequence of their deteriorating condition, but it may be that the concern has some validity. Family members can be very intuitive, feeling that things are not quite right, but they may be wrong of course, especially if they do not have the full information.

Following the Francis report into the Mid Staffordshire Hospital Trust there is now a requirement for trusts in England to demonstrate a duty of candour to be open, honest and truthful. There should be the same transparency in care homes. It may be hard for leaders to tell relatives that the home may have failed the resident in some way, and to face the families' anger and demands for a full explanation, but families and residents deserve honesty. If families feel they have not been told the truth or have been given an explanation using words that avoid the facts, they will become even more angry.

Families who feel aggrieved or lied to are more likely to pursue their complaint through local and national complaints procedures, sometimes resorting to legal action through the courts. There is the anecdotal opinion that people make negligence claims because of the 'no win no fee', ambulance-chasing culture that has travelled across the Atlantic from America. However McIvery and Wyndham (2013) contest this view. They quote G K Chesterton who described success in the court as a stiff apology saying: "A stiff apology is a second insult… The injured party does not want to be compensated because he has been wronged, he wants to be healed because he has been hurt." (McIvery & Wyndham 2013).

In healthcare settings the concept of an 'ethical emergency' has been examined. In the book *After the Error* which addressed the issue of how patient safety could save lives ((McIvery & Wyndham 2013), Dr Herbert defined an ethical emergency as one where there is the potential for a complete loss of trust in the health care professionals and health care organisation by the survivors. The longer the failure to explain and apologise continued, the greater the chasm between the survivors and the professionals. There is the potential for this situation occurring in all unexpected death scenarios, whether or not the deaths were preventable (McIvery & Wyndham 2013). Although these views were expressed about hospital care the observations are relevant to care homes because they are about the appropriate response to concerns or poor outcomes, and how the failure to address them immediately only makes the concerns worse. These failures add layers of mistrust and animosity that can cause a complete relationship breakdown in the home.

If a concern is being investigated the leader should keep the family fully informed about progress, preferably talking to them face to face if at all possible. During the investigation the leader must ensure staff do not develop a defensive attitude towards the family. Not only will this harm the relationship but it could cause the family to become more suspicious of both home and staff. Many families fear repercussions if they complain so it is important staff understand that relatives have this right to complain if they are concerned, and that there will be no question of repercussions for either the resident or the family.

EXAMPLE

Bert was having a respite break in a residential care home. His daughter discovered there were no night staff employed in the home and the home owners simply listened to the residents in their rooms via intercom. She complained to the regulator who immediately investigated. The same day the home owner evicted Bert with immediate effect because of the trouble his daughter had caused. The regulator followed due process and closed the home.

On occasions it may be that the home needs to raise concerns with the family, perhaps about how family members are behaving in the home or towards their relative because of a change in her/his condition. The leader should gather all the information before meeting with the family to ensure there are no misunderstandings, and to be certain that staff have been factual and accurate in their description of the situation. During the meeting the leader should focus on the needs of the resident and be clear that the home's suggestions are evidence based and in the resident's best interests (if they lack capacity). There are legal processes available that can be used to protect the resident against relatives if necessary, and the leader has a duty to pursue these if appropriate. In extreme situations the leader can raise a safeguarding concern and involve other professionals in order to protect the resident.

The resident's right to say no to a relative

Relatives do not have an automatic right to see a resident if the resident does not want to see them. Staff should always encourage the resident to make the decision that best suits them, and occasionally that may be to say 'no' to some members of their family. Equally, staff should be vigilant about relatives removing property and valuables from a resident's room. The resident may be happy to give away valuables or money to family or friends, but the staff must gently establish that this is their true wish and that they are not being coerced in some way. If necessary, local safeguarding procedures should be implemented to enable a full and thorough enquiry.

POINTERS FOR PREVENTION OF ABUSE

1 Primary prevention
General activities, for example...

Give both staff and families the same, clear information about how the home wants them to communicate and work together as well as the role of the key worker. By giving staff the same information as residents, everything is open and clear.

2 Secondary prevention
Specific activities, for example...

Hold relatives meetings and be open and honest. Ask relatives for suggestions and solutions to concerns that may have an organisational impact.

3 Tertiary prevention
A response to an actual situation, for example...

If there is a safeguarding investigation, keep the families fully informed and be as open and honest as possible.

Chapter 9
Safeguarding enquiries: investigate and be thorough and fair

One difficulty of being the leader of a team which usually has a close and positive working relationship is when there has to be an investigation into a complaint about the care delivered by the team, or one member of the team. The language of investigation may be different depending on the country where the care home is located. The Care Act refers to the need for an enquiry, rather than investigation, as this latter term is thought to have the potential to cause confusion with investigations carried out by the police. However a Section 42 (Care Act 2014) safeguarding enquiry is a process which may include an investigation such as a police investigation, a serious incident investigation or a disciplinary investigation. Although the language may be different depending on the legal framework of the country this chapter will use the term 'enquiry' to describe a safeguarding investigation. This chapter will describe how the leader can undertake an enquiry into a safeguarding concern that has been raised.

Adult safeguarding policy
The legislative framework for safeguarding has been set out in Chapter 1. Whether the care home leader will undertake a safeguarding enquiry will depend on the local arrangements. However, the skills required to carry out a safeguarding enquiry can be applied to any type of investigation, whether it is a complaint, disciplinary or serious incident investigation.

The care leader has a responsibility:

- to be familiar with the national legislative framework
- to be familiar with the relevant multi-agency procedures
- to ensure the home's safeguarding policy is in tune with the home's overarching policies
- to give clear direction to staff about internal actions to protect the adult at risk
- to explain to staff how an enquiry is carried out if required.

When is a concern or complaint a safeguarding matter?

The question of what constitutes a safeguarding concern as opposed to a clinical incident or a complaint continues to cause difficulties. Again the criteria for referral vary from council to council. Some require all incidents to be referred while others appear to ignore even those which could be considered serious.

There is also variation between the requirements for NHS providers and the care home sector. Despite the Department of Health issuing guidance to help differentiate between a clinical incident and a safeguarding concern, there continue to be differences between what is expected of the NHS and what is expected of safeguarding in a care home (Phair & Manthorpe, 2011).

An audit of clinical incidents and disciplinary outcomes and incident reports in the NHS found that there was a very low referral rate, both for safeguarding and to the Disclosure and Barring Service, from the NHS compared with the care sector (Phair & Manthorpe 2011). Some clinical incidents identified in the audit were reviewed by a multidisciplinary expert panel which confirmed that some of the clinical incidents were routinely not referred as safeguarding concerns, and the person responsible for the incident was not investigated using the disciplinary processes.

EXAMPLE

Examples of how the NHS failed to investigate serious safeguarding incidents included a doctor who had lied about seeing a patient who suffered harm, and another of multiple concerns about care on a ward (Phair & Manthorpe, 2011). By contrast there is anecdotal evidence about how a care home in the Midlands was investigated and found to have neglected a resident because the staff forgot to order some blood glucose monitoring sticks. They realised their error and immediately ordered some, notifying the resident's GP who agreed they should test the urine. The resident's diabetes was found to be stable and there were no adverse effects. The nurse correctly recorded the omission and the adjusted action required in the care plan. This record was noticed by a NHS nurse who referred the matter as a safeguarding concern which resulted in the local authority substantiating an allegation of neglect.

Approaches to the enquiry

There are no defined approaches to undertaking a safeguarding enquiry. It is very important that the resident, as the adult at risk, stays central to the enquiry. They should be fully consulted and give their consent, if they are able to understand what is being undertaken. The outcome they desire from the enquiry should be taken as the focus of the enquiry, if at all possible.

There is a dilemma and potential conflict if the resident decides they do not want any enquiry or action to be taken. In a care home, while a particular resident's view would have to be taken into consideration, the duty of care is to act in the public interest which in the case of a care home would be the interests of the other residents. It may be, therefore, that this particular resident's wishes have to be overruled. If the resident lacked capacity the next of kin should be informed and kept abreast of developments.

The NHS uses the root cause analysis (RCA) process (www.NPSA.nhs.uk). This is designed to identify the root causes of an error or omission of care and focuses on any systems failure. For example, a root cause analysis will establish the system that failed and caused a person to develop a pressure ulcer or why a person was not given enough to drink, but it would not necessarily identify whether neglect had occurred or whether others are at risk. It also does not identify any individuals who may need to be 'helped to account for their actions'. Brown (2009) expresses concern that the linear model of the RCA presupposes a cause of error to fit into an individual or contained problem; meaning that the approach does not allow for wider issues to be considered. The RCA looks simply at the originally identified issue.

Balancing the need for an enquiry: keeping the resident safe and supporting the staff

The focus of any safeguarding enquiry must primarily be about the needs and safety of the resident. However, that does not mean that the legal and moral rights of the staff members allegedly involved should be ignored or overlooked. Any type of investigation can be an anxious time for the staff involved. Unnecessary anxiety caused by the process of the enquiry should be avoided it at all possible. The staff involved can be supported by:

- informing them about the concerns, giving them as much information as it is safe and reasonable to do. How much information can be given will be determined by the details and nature of the concern
- trying to ensure the process is as swift and efficient as possible, without compromising thoroughness and due diligence
- not prejudging the outcome or allowing a negative attitude to intrude during the enquiry
- listening carefully to what the staff member (or team) says and clarifying the information they are being given, if necessary
- giving the staff member(s) an opportunity to confirm that the information included in the enquiry is correct from their perspective
- offering the staff member(s) an avenue of expert support from outside the home
- ensuring the staff member(s) are treated in a manner that the investigator would like to be treated themselves should they be under investigation.

Enquiry procedure

The suggested approach to undertaking an enquiry applies to whoever is allocated the role of the enquiry officer. This role could be taken by the care leader.

An enquiry into something that has already happened, for example an allegation that a carer shouted at a resident, will require the investigator to ensure any actions undertaken have followed the appropriate procedure as directed by the local safeguarding policy.

If it is agreed that the best person to undertake the enquiry is the care leader the following principles should be applied and steps taken:

- talk to the resident (if possible) to establish what outcome they want from the enquiry. They can be supported by their family or an advocate, whoever they feel is the most appropriate
- talk to any witnesses and the person allegedly responsible for the concern(s). The worker can have a person with them as support, and make sure they both see the information that has been recorded about the meeting, and are given a copy of it. Interviewing the staff involved should follow the local human resources procedures
- review any other information that may assist, for example the resident's care plan
- form an opinion about whether, on the balance of probability, the allegation was true, untrue or unsubstantiated.

The outcome of the safeguarding enquiry may mean the worker is referred into disciplinary procedures, but the enquiry is not in itself a disciplinary procedure. The care leader must ensure that correct disciplinary procedures are followed and, while working in accordance with the multi-agency safeguarding procedures, should not allow the rights of the worker to be undermined. There may be some (or many) who believe that the worker should be suspended pending the outcome of the enquiry but this can only be done by the employer.

Undertaking a safeguarding enquiry

A care home leader may be required to undertake an enquiry into allegations of any type of alleged abuse. However the most complicated to investigate can be an allegation that a resident has been neglected. Examples of neglect include:

- neglect in respect of care, food and fluids
- weight loss due to poor nutrition
- the resident's increasing agitation due to constipation or poor pain control has been ignored
- the development of pressure ulcers because appropriate care has not been carried out
- incorrect or inconsistent administration of medication.

Any concern of alleged neglect should be reported to the service regulator, the commissioner, the family (with resident's agreement) and the local authority.

EXAMPLE

For the purposes of this book an example of an enquiry into unexplained weight loss will be used and it will be assumed that it is in the resident's best interests that the concerns are investigated.

Understanding the causes of the concern

Three key questions an investigator should always consider:

- Does the story match the facts?
- Can the condition of the resident be explained by alternative clinical reasons?
- Are others at risk?

Sources of information

The leader, in their capacity as the investigator, should ensure that all available information is obtained. Information can be obtained from numerous sources and will include asking questions. The information should include:

- information about any past medical history which might explain weight loss
- current medical conditions that might affect nutrition
- any recent illness that might have caused weight loss
- weight records
- nutritional risk assessment and care plan. What does the care plan say and how well has it been carried out by staff? Has everything been done to support the resident's nutrition?
- the extent of family involvement. Has the family been involved and have they been consulted about the resident's favourite foods? Has the appropriate information been recorded? Have the favourite foods been offered?
- food charts. Have any changes in the resident's weight been appropriately referred for expert advice Including referral to the resident's or care home's GP? Has the opinion of any specialist been requested, if appropriate? Is there evidence of the involvement of a dietician?
- evidence that the staff who worked with the resident helped the resident to eat and drink, including a note about any obstacles that might have prevented them from helping appropriately
- evidence of how the kitchen fortifies food and which residents receive it. It might be appropriate to talk to the chef to establish what procedures are used and whether they conform with established practice
- evidence of a review of the resident's medication charts and whether any medication taken by the resident could affect appetite.

Additional sources of information to build a broader perspective

- previous care records
- current care records including risk assessments, care plans and records of medications
- medical records, GP records (with GP or hospital permission)
- management records (such as accident reports, health and safety records, staff rotas)
- menus, food and fluid intake
- records of visiting professionals
- decor, aroma and hygiene of the care setting
- general atmosphere
- inspection reports for the care setting.

Laboratory tests

If neglect is suspected, some laboratory tests may assist in defining the cause of a person's condition. Examples include:

- blood urea, electrolytes, creatine and urine analysis – used to measure hydration status
- metabolic screens – used to detect nutritional or endocrine abnormalities
- complete blood count and coagulation studies – used to detect excessively easy bruising
- drug levels – used to detect under or over medication
- toxicology screens – used to detect substance abuse or use of under-reported medications.

Reviewing the care records

The investigator will examine the care home's records closely and consider whether:

- they have been completed in accordance with the care home's policies and procedures or accepted current practice
- whether there are entries for the whole timeframe or whether there are any gaps
- whether entries may have been added to or amended later to appear in a better light
- whether the assessments link correctly with the care plan
- whether the care plan has been carried out.

Gathering information

The decision about who will lead or support a discussion, and who will be asked to attend a meeting, should be agreed at the initial strategy meeting or by agreement with the safeguarding enquiry manager. If the police are leading the enquiry, they may ask for a nurse to be present to advise them on professional or clinical matters.

There may be a variety of people who the investigator needs to talk to. The investigator is not 'interviewing' anyone. They are having discussions about the topic, either generally or specifically in order to inform the enquiry. The resident involved may be able to give information about their weight loss, food and dietary intake. They might be supported by their family, or an independent advocate. However if the discussion is informal it may be less intrusive to have a lower-key chat.

Staff who are involved in catering may be able to give valuable information about systems and processes, while direct care staff may be able to give information about the resident and about how food and meals are managed in the home.

Preparation of the person who will be asked to give information

There are simple steps to follow to ensure any enquiry is open and transparent, and all those involved understand the reasons why. The following are suggestions for best practice when arranging a meeting with staff. Ensure participants:

• have details of, and written confirmation of, the venue and timing
• know they have the right to have someone support them
• are aware of the process and what stage it is at
• know what the procedure is going to be
• know why they are being interviewed
• know what the complaint/allegation is
• know that notes will be taken and shown to them and they can correct any errors (and possibly sign them) and be given a copy.

Styles of asking questions

Police and social workers are trained in a questioning style which enables them to 'achieve best evidence.' Care leaders who are undertaking an enquiry may not have had specific training, but the principles apply in all information-gathering situations.

There are four phases of information-gathering for achieving best evidence:

1. establish rapport

2. take part in free narrative

3. ask questions

4. closure and summary.

Generally open-ended questions should be asked as they tend to elicit more information than closed questions, and it is important not to pre-judge the information that might be forthcoming.

Triangulating the information

The analysis or consideration of the information gathered is checked and cross referenced by the investigator in a process called triangulation. At this point it will be possible to form an opinion about whether the resident's weight loss was avoidable or not, and whether everything reasonable had been done to prevent the weight loss. The decision about whether the resident was neglected may not be required to be made by the investigator, but might be considered at the case conference, depending on local policy.

The investigator's report should be clear and unambiguous so that anyone reading the report can follow the 'story' and be able to see where the evidence came from. It may also be helpful to reference local or national policies or best practice. This type of reference gives strength to the report and supports the investigator's arguments, and gives credence to the evidence, effectively demonstrating that it's not just one person's opinion.

Neglect, poor care – or a sad consequence of the resident's condition?

Having collected all the available information and analysed it, the findings may be presented at a multi-agency meeting. Whenever the findings are considered and there is a discussion about whether the allegation of neglect is true or untrue, the decision-making process can be assisted by using the determinants of neglect (Phair & Heath, 2009):

- What is the current situation of the resident, and what have been the consequences or impact on them of the alleged behaviour?
- What exactly did the caregiver fail to do?
- Should the caregiver have known what to do? Was it reasonable to expect the caregiver to know how to care for the resident?
- Did the caregiver take all reasonable steps to try and prevent the resident losing weight?

There can be three possible outcomes:

1. If staff did everything they could to prevent weight loss, followed procedures, sought assistance, undertaken assessments, followed care plans, given fortified and supplement foods, and kept clear and detailed records, it can be concluded that the weight loss was a sad consequence of the resident's condition.
2. If staff failed to undertake important aspects of care to prevent weight loss, and the assessment and record keeping is poor, but the resident has not suffered any harm, or the weight loss was not as significant as alleged, the conclusion could be that it is poor care but not neglect.
3. If the staff failed to undertake important aspects of care to prevent weight loss, kept poor records, and failed to seek assistance to try and manage the weight loss and the resident suffered harm, perhaps including increased weakness, confusion, constipation, urinary infections and falls, all of which could be compounded or caused by poor dietary and fluid intake, then the outcome could be concluded as neglect.

Human factors, apportioning blame or holding to account?

As part of the conclusions at the safeguarding meeting, consideration should be given to the reasons why someone was harmed. This will assist in considering the best safeguarding action plan. As part of this review, human factors should be considered.

Discussion continues in the literature about the negative impact of a blame culture which it is believed, as an approach, does no more than seek people out in order to hold them responsible and take the blame for an incident or error. Taking the blame has a negative focus and implies that the person had no responsibility for the harm caused to the person, but was simply the person who was the 'scapegoat'. Yet taking the blame should imply the person accepts responsibility for their part in any failing of care. Work on human errors in health care supports the need to establish not only what went wrong, but why it went wrong and how it went wrong. Caring for people is inherently a risky business and things can go wrong with the task and equipment, however hard staff try to prevent it.

Errors can be caused by:

- a worker making a mistake during an intended action or procedure leading to an error
- lapses or slips caused by memory failure, or a skill-based error, meaning a worker is responsible for unintended actions
- a worker violating the rules (fails to do what they should have done or does something they should not have done) due to recklessness or malicious actions.

Proponents of human factors in healthcare recognise that we can all make mistakes as we are all human. Based on this concept there are five types of human error, as described by Miller and Swain in Ootim (2002):

1. **errors of omission** – something should have been done that wasn't
2. **errors of commission** – something that should not have been done was (rules were broken)
3. **extraneous acts** – something is done that prevents something else happening
4. **sequential errors** – a task is performed with the sequence in the wrong order
5. **time errors** – the correct action was performed either too early or too late.

The problem with human error models when looking at omissions in practice is that the impact on the resident is not considered. The error or harm caused is only considered from the worker's perspective.

Justification or mitigation

It is important to establish the reasons why a person did not receive the care they needed so it can be decided what should happen to the staff who failed the resident. The language of the human factors in healthcare principles (as described above) gives an insight into why things sometimes happen, but describing the reasons why they happened is never enough to justify the pain and suffering caused. It does not make it any more bearable for the agitated, confused resident who has developed a chest infection to know that the reason for their suffering is because there were only two staff on duty and they could not care for 24 residents to the standard required.

The information about why the resident was neglected should be used only in mitigation. It offers a reasonable explanation why the two staff on duty should not be held personally accountable since they had been forced into an unacceptable situation by senior managers or perhaps the home owner. It places responsibility and accountability squarely on senior management. Common mitigating factors include lack of staff, poor working conditions, weak leadership, staff victimisation or personal circumstances (Stevens *et al* 2008).

Reckless practice and unintentional neglect

When considering the outcome of an enquiry it is important to consider what the term 'reckless' means. It means that the person failed to do what was reasonable to expect them to do, and that there was no evidence to suggest they tried to put things right. They simply 'didn't bother' to try to make the situation right. Additionally, to meet the definition of neglect in the Care Act (2014), there is no requirement for inaction or omission to be deliberate or intentional. It is sufficient for the purpose of determining neglect if it can be shown that it was reasonable to expect the worker to have known what to do.

In the Civil Courts of England and Wales the Bolam Test is applied (*Bolam v Fiern Hospital Management Committee*, 1957 [www.wikipedia.org]). This is a useful guide for any enquiry into safeguarding concerns. The tests ask whether the acts or omissions fall below the standard expected of a responsible body of medical people or similar professionals. In other words, did the staff member fail to carry out the necessary care? or carry out care which fell below the standard expected of their level of knowledge and skills. For example it would be wrong to expect a care assistant to know as much as a nurse, but it would be reasonable to expect a care assistant to ask a nurse what should be done or report concerns about a resident's condition.

The standard of proof

The standard of proof in any enquiry is the balance of probability. This means that the evidence should suggest to the investigator that it is more likely than not that the act or omission occurred. The decision is not based on the criminal test of 'beyond reasonable doubt'.

The risks to other residents

The leader who has identified neglect of care happening to one resident should be mindful that it may have occurred with others too. It is not an automatic consequence, however, and the risk of others being neglected in the same way will depend on a number of factors:

- What was the type of neglect and could it have affected other residents? For example, dehydration is the type of neglect which could affect any resident but poor management of diabetes would only be a concern to other residents who were diabetic.
- Did the enquiry identify serious harm to the resident? What is the likelihood of others being at risk?

If there are any concerns about other residents, the leader should review their care and put urgent safeguarding plans in place.

Holding staff to account

The action taken against staff will depend on their direct involvement in the neglect, their attitude and their level of accountability. The principle of 'holding to account' is to ensure staff take personal responsibility for the part they played in the neglect and that they learn and act more responsibly in the future. It could vary from supportive reflective supervision to helping the staff understand their role in the failings, It does not mean that staff should automatically be disciplined or referred to the Disclosure and Barring Service although that may be necessary in some cases.

Enquiries conducted by outside agencies

The enquiry may be conducted by the statutory agencies, if this is the local policy. Leaders should always co-operate with the enquiry process, but should also be confident that the agency conducting the enquiry is following the local procedures correctly and is working in partnership with the home. If the police are involved in an enquiry their processes will supersede a local authority enquiry until their investigation is completed. If the police are not involved it is reasonable to expect the local authority to work in partnership with the home to progress the enquiry in a timely manner. The local authority must ensure that due process is followed and that the requirement of natural justice is applied.

In a judicial review in 2012 the judge upheld a complaint that West Sussex County Council had not applied natural justice to the investigative process in respect of alleged neglect at Nyton House (Hewitt 2013 – *Davis and Davis v West Sussex County Council*, 2012). The outcome was that the findings were required to be quashed and set aside. Natural justice applies where public (and other) bodies make decisions. The precise form the rules take depends on the body in question but in the case of *Davis and Davis v West Sussex County Council* the rules were identified thus:

- if a public body has the power to make decisions affecting individuals, it must follow set procedures and should act in the way it has 'promised' (as set out in a policy)
- natural justice implies the right to be heard, which includes the right to know what evidence has been given, what statements have been made and have a fair opportunity to challenge them
- everyone should have the right to prepare their case
- everyone should have the right to call evidence on their own behalf (Hewitt 2013).

While it is important that leaders ensure that their organisation is not mistreated by the process and that there is natural justice, a leader also has a professional responsibility to honestly examine the concerns and act to minimise any risks to residents if there is evidence that harm has occurred, and has a duty to comply with local safeguarding processes.

POINTERS FOR PREVENTION OF ABUSE

1 Primary prevention
General activities, for example…

Make information openly available to staff and families about how to raise a concern. The information could include internal procedures, local authority and CQC procedures, and also information about national organisations such as Concern at Work, the Relatives & Residents Association or Independent Age.

2 Secondary prevention
Specific activities, for example…

Appoint an external 'concern at work ambassador' who staff can contact to discuss concerns. The ambassador must have the authority to raise concerns on behalf of the staff and oversee and scrutinise any enquiry.

3 Tertiary prevention
A response to an actual situation, for example…

Set up a system of reflecting on the outcome of an enquiry with the individuals involved, not just in respect of standard human resource processes, but to enable them to examine their own contribution to the incident and how they could have acted differently.

Chapter 10
Systems, processes and monitoring to prevent abuse

Care home leaders have a highly responsible and vital role in upholding the standards of care and practice, setting the tone for the culture of care there and raising the expectations of all staff. Any home could become the subject of a safeguarding concern which, if proved, could leave the leaders and other staff shocked and stunned that abusive practice was going on and no one suspected anything.

Every chapter in this book includes ideas and suggestions, as well as thought-provoking perspectives which offer guidance on how to reduce the risk of abuse occurring, enhancing the prevention and resilience model of safeguarding and building a positive culture of care where staff take pride in themselves and their work.

In addition to the themes covered throughout the book, the leader can adopt a safeguarding approach to information that is already routinely available. When considered from a safeguarding perspective, this could offer evidence to indicate suitable preventative activity to uphold a positive culture of care.

Organisational factors that support a positive care culture

The PANICOA report *Respect and Protect* identified a number of key attributes which would suggest a care culture is strong:

- **Person-centredness is a core value** – positive care experiences are more likely to occur where there is a strong organisational understanding of residents' specific needs and a clear strategy for their care. Person-centredness is not just about responding to individual needs but about taking active steps to include individuals in decisions about care, as well as their families. The more families are engaged, the better the person-centred care is. If the person centred approach runs through all roles and departments in the organisation, and staff feel they too are valued in a person centred way, this core value will be shared and upheld.
- **The capability for change is strong** –ie a strong culture exists, where the leader manages change effectively using:
  - excellent internal support systems
  - ways of cushioning the impact of change on staff from external factors
  - support for change translation into better practice.

- **The leadership is strong and visible** – leaders are visible and proactive at all levels, leading by example and encouraging positive care experiences. Leaders who are able to make decisions and take responsibility within clearly defined boundaries are likely to increase the commitment of staff to excellent care. Strong leadership is needed to ensure core values are upheld.
- **Staff are valued, supported and motivated** – valuing and supporting staff is central to maintaining a stable workforce. Staff should be valued – just as residents are – and given opportunities to be involved in the development of the caring culture. A culture of trust and openness in which staff feel able to make suggestions for change, or express concerns, has a real opportunity to nip problems in the bud.
- **The physical resource is effectively managed** – financial success is not the only factor which indicates a positive care culture exists. The layout of the home, facilities and decor are all important.
- **The organisation is connected** – all departments are well and seamlessly connected with a strong team ethic which supports continuity and consistency in care. Organisations which are well connected to the wider health or social care community are less likely to suffer from the organisational isolation which so easily can have a negative impact on the quality of care.
- **An active learning culture** – an organisation prepared to try new ideas and learn from the past, or able to anticipate and avoid potential risks, will create a positive care culture. Organisations resistant to new evidence of good practice or with entrenched attitudes are more at risk of creating the poor culture of care which can result in abuse occurring.

Indicators that may be suggesting organisational abuse or neglect

Leaders at all levels should be mindful of the risk factors that may indicate the care culture is becoming neglectful or organisationally abusive. If the risks are recognised early and dealt with, a positive care culture can be restored before harm occurs.

During the development of the 'PIECE-dem' observational framework, Brooker *et al* (2011) identified key indicators of possible neglect and abuse in an older person living with dementia in a care home as:

- withdrawn, depressed behaviour
- increased levels of emotional distress
- the care giver's response to the resident tends to be negative
- the facial expression of the resident shows, for example, anxiety, depression or hopelessness
- there is reduced diet and fluid intake
- the quality of interaction between staff and the resident is poor
- there is little interaction between people in the care environment
- the resident has reduced levels of physical activity and social engagement

- the resident has few opportunities to participate in activities of daily life
- the resident's privacy is not respected
- there are locks on doors and other restraints.

Phair (2009) undertook a review of more than 250 individual assessments of older people completed as part of safeguarding investigations in organisational settings. The review focused on the health and personal care needs of the older people. The most common and/or repeated symptoms and signs of people who were neglected were identified as:

- dehydration
- inadequate nutrition
- infections, including thrush, acquired in the care setting
- constipation/faecal incontinence
- intractable pain and/or poor pain management
- insomnia coupled with the resident often appearing to be in a twilight state or excessively drowsy
- confusion not linked to the resident's diagnosed mental condition
- the resident showing a sense of hopelessness and/or resignation
- recurrent falls without cause
- the presence of pressure ulcers
- the resident becoming acutely ill, or a long-term condition becoming worse.

Any of these conditions can occur spontaneously (without any hint of neglect) depending on the complexity of the person's illness. Equally they could be caused by neglect. As far as the case for abuse having occurred, the defining factor is what was done to prevent these common complications of frailty taking place.

EXAMPLE

A care home regularly performed well during regulatory inspections; staff had all the required competencies and residents rarely experienced complications of frailty such as chest infections or pressure ulcers. However, families would often talk to the leader about 'little niggles'. The leader decided to undertake an observation in the care setting and identified the attitude of staff as being 'cold' and rather officious, although very efficient, thereby creating an atmosphere of tension and anxiety for residents and relatives.

Moving forward and taking action

As already stated in this book and as identified during the PANICOA research referred to earlier, the leader needs to be assertive, approachable and pro-active. S/he already has a great deal of valuable information at her/his fingertips but the key is to start considering it all from a safeguarding perspective. This perspective will greatly reduce the risk of a safeguarding concern developing by ensuring the care leader is enabling a positive culture of care to thrive.

50 good practice tips on promoting a positive culture of care and reducing the risk of neglect and organisational abuse

- Praise staff and celebrate care and compassion by highlighting the tiniest things that make the biggest difference.
- Start a 'Be proud' diary and encourage everyone to write examples of things that occur that made them feel proud at work on any given day.
- The leader needs to have a high level of current knowledge about the kind of care being offered in the home, as well as its legal framework and organisational requirements.
- The leader needs to be visible, and not just 9 to 5, Monday to Friday. Set the standards and be a role model.
- Have an open door and always take the concerns of others seriously. Staff who feel they are valued will uphold the appropriate culture of care, preventing abusive activity as best they can and reporting it if it occurs.
- Listen and link concerns that may seem small or insignificant on their own. It may be that a picture of abuse is there to be seen. Do not think of issues in isolation. Ensure the response or action is proportionate to the concern.
- Build good relationships with external professionals. They will be able to offer positive practice that you can pass onto staff.
- Equally important is building good relationships with staff so that, if necessary, they will feel able to inform you about concerns that may be based on feelings or conversations. If there is not a good and trusting relationship they will not have the confidence to talk to you.
- Keep in close contact with families and invite them to relatives' meetings, ideally run by an external facilitator.
- Listen to families' smallest concerns, and consider them all carefully.
- Provide active staff supervision as well as encouraging personal development. Consider staff reactions to opportunities to learn new skills or new ideas – are they enthusiastic?
- Ensure the care home's policies and procedures are easy to access, readable and understandable. Review their effectiveness, particularly if they have not been followed.
- Do walkabouts and look at the environments through the eyes of the resident. Is it clean, or perhaps noisy, even malodorous, or too hot or too cold? Do walkabouts at different times of the day and night to obtain a full picture.

- Ask the staff for feedback on how they feel the various departments in the home are supporting the residents and ask if there are any obstacles to staff carrying out their job.
- Think about whether notices are appropriate in residents' own rooms. Remember the room is their home not a treatment room.
- Check pressure-relieving mattresses and audit whether they are on the correct setting. Put the residents' weight chart in their room for easy reference – but not on public display.
- Look at the record charts and review if they have been completed accurately, and in a timely manner. Note if the charts are easily accessible for staff, families or the residents to complete.
- Ensure the staff know how much fluid the home's cups hold so they can accurately gauge the residents' fluid input.
- Ensure staff understand the importance of completing repositioning charts correctly.
- Encourage staff to have the correct manual handling equipment in the right place with correct attachments.
- Audit the medicine charts and review whether residents are given 'as required medicines' routinely? If they are, ask why.
- Ask the community pharmacist to undertake a medicines audit and report if they have any issues.
- Spend time working in different departments, so you can understand different staff members' perspectives.
- Review all admissions to hospital and look for any patterns. Could any admissions have been avoided if care had been delivered differently?
- Review whether there are patterns relating to emergency admissions to hospital from floors of the home or by different staff members.
- Review the incident reports to try to identify any patterns regarding location, time of incidents and staff involved.
- Review incidents reporting distressed resident behaviour for any patterns regarding time, activity or staff involved.
- Consider if the attitude of the staff could have contributed to distressed resident behaviour.
- Involve the chef in care planning to improve residents' calorie intake and choice of food.
- Review the care plans and audit the accuracy of the assessments and whether care practices are appropriate.
- Review the daily records for evidence of changes in residents' conditions and what actions were taken.
- Discuss with staff the action they took in response to changes in residents' conditions and their reasons.
- Set up systems to involve staff in auditing and reviewing care practices.
- Support the staff by identifying and trying to resolve problems with outside agencies.
- Hold regular staff meetings for each department within the home.
- Set up a quality circle to support innovative practices.
- Visit the home at night and listen and learn how the night staff work and what their challenges are.

- Keep records of when concerns are raised with senior managers and outside agencies.
- Keep senior managers briefed about any adverse incidents or emerging patterns which might suggest there are safeguarding issues.
- Be aware that close relationships between team members can cloud judgements if questions arise about a staff member's attitude or competence.
- Introduce a care and compassion observation tool such as the Sit & See™ tool.
- Develop a team of observers to help with audits.
- Publish and, whenever possible, celebrate the results of positive audits.
- Encourage staff to organise social events and try to attend them yourself.
- Keep senior managers informed of any social events and invite them to attend.
- Develop a wide network of professionals who can offer support and advice.
- Encourage staff to feel it does not reflect badly on them to ask 'silly' questions.
- Sit and listen to the sounds of the home and reflect on whether it sounds a happy home.
- Make a point of asking different members of staff what they have done today which makes them 'feel proud'.
- Chat with at least one resident a day, have a little fun with them and laugh a lot.

At the end of each day think back about any positive or kind or compassionate action which you saw, heard and felt. When you are having a tough day and it feels like it is all going wrong, think of the residents who have had a positive experience. Remember the laughter, feel the love and care and celebrate how positive leadership can safeguard residents from abuse.

POINTERS FOR PREVENTION OF ABUSE

1 Primary prevention
General activities, for example...

Create a list of all routinely gathered information which shows that the home is offering positive, safe care, and put it on the notice board.

2 Secondary prevention
Specific activities, for example...

Develop a 'safeguarding walkabout' checklist, and engage staff from different departments to complete it at agreed frequencies. Feed the observations back at staff meetings.

3 Tertiary prevention
A response to an actual situation, for example...

Following completion of a complaint, safeguarding or clinical incident enquiry, map any findings against previous incidents and consider if there are themes, trends or areas of concern which need to be addressed.

References

Adult Protection Fora (2013) *Wales Policy and Procedures for the Protection of Vulnerable Adults from Abuse*.

Age Concern (2006) *Hungry to be Heard*. Age Concern England
http://www.scie.org.uk/publications/guides/guide15/files/hungrytobeheard.pdf

Baker R (2003) *A review of deaths at Gosport Memorial Hospital*. University of Leicester
https://www.gov.uk/government/uploads/system/uploads/attachment_data/file/226263/review_
gosport_war_memorial_hospital.pdf

Brooker D, La Fontaine J, De Vries K, Porter T (2011) *'How can I tell you what's going on here?' The
development of PIECE-dem: An observational framework to bring to light the perspective of residents with
advanced dementia living in care homes*. University of Worcester – Association of Dementia Studies.

Buckinghamshire (2013) *Safer Recruitment tool kit*. Buckingham Safeguarding Vulnerable Adult Board.
www.buckinghamshirepartnership.gov.uk.

Cavendish C (2013) *'The Cavendish Review'. An independent review into health care assistants and support
workers in the NHS and social care settings*. HM Government, London.

Commission for Health Improvement Investigations (2003) *Investigation into matters arising from care on
Rowan ward*, Manchester Mental Health & Social Care Trust.
http://www.elderabuse.org.uk/Documents/Other%20Orgs/Abuse%20Report%20-
CHI%20Rowan%20Ward.pdf

Chochinor H M (2007) Dignity and the essence of medicine: The A, B, C and D of dignity conserving care.
British Medical Journal 335, 7612, 184-187.

Cuthbert A.S. (2013) in Hehir B, Report 'A crisis of compassion: Who cares? Battle of ideas 20-21 October
2012, London. *Nursing Ethics* 20(1) 109-114.

Department of Health & Home office (2000) *No Secrets: Guidance on developing and implementing multi-
agency policies and procedures to protect vulnerable adults from abuse*. HM Government, London.

Department of Health (2012) *Compassion in Practice: Nursing, Midwifery and Care staff: our vision and
strategy*. The Stationary Office, London.

Department of Health (2012) *Decision Support Tool for NHS Continuing Health Care*. HM Government, London.

Department of Health (2013) *Hard Truths: The Journey to putting Patients First. Volume 1*. The Stationary
Office, London.

Department of Health (2014) *Care and Support Statutory Guidance. Issued under the Care Act 2014*. Crown
copyright London

Dewar B (2011) Caring about caring: an appreciative enquiry about compassionate relationship centred care in Dewar 2013.

Dewar B (2013) Cultivating compassionate care. *Nursing Standard* 27, 34, 48-55.

Dewar B, Christley Y (2013) A critical analysis of compassion in practice. *Nursing Standard* 28, 10, 46-50.

Drucker p (2001) *Essential Drucker: Management, the Individual and Society.* Butterworth-Heinemann Ltd.

Ford P, Heath H, McCormack B, Phair L (2004) *What a difference a nurse makes.* Royal College of Nursing, London.

Francis R (2013) *Report of the Mid Staffordshire NHS Foundation Trust Public Inquiry.* The Stationary office, London.

Georgiou N (2014) *Orchid View Serious Case Review.* West Sussex Adults Safeguarding Board.

Hamson S, Hunter D, Monson G, and Pollitt C (1992) *Just managing power and culture in the NHS.* Macmillan, London.

Handy C (1986) *Understanding organisations 3rd Edn.* Penguin, Harmondsworth.

Hayes H, Whitney J (2014) True cost of care. *Nursing Older People* 26, 5, 12.

Heath H & Phair L (2009) The concept of frailty and its significance in the consequences of care or neglect for older people: an analysis. *International Journal of Older People Nursing* 4,120-131.

Hewitt D (2013) Her treatment at and around the meeting was deplorable: Might safeguarding itself constitute abuse? *The Journal of Adult Protection* 15, 2, 96-105.

Janis J L, & Mann L (1977) *Decision Making: A psychological analysis of conflict, choice and commitment.* New York: Free Press.

Killett A, Burns D, et al (2012) *Organisational Dynamics of Respect and Elder Care.* PANICOA.

Killett A, Bowes A, Brooker D *et al* (2013) *What makes a difference to resident experience? Digging deep into care home culture: The CHOICE (Care Home Organisations Implementing Cultures of Excellence) research report.* PANICOA.

Lupton C, Croft-White C (2013) *Respect and Protect: The experience of older people and staff in care homes and hospitals.* The PANICOA Report – Comic Relief.

Manthorpe J, Stevens M, Hussein S, Heath H, Lievesley N (2011) *The abuse, neglect and mistreatment of older people in care homes and hospitals in England: Observations on the potential for secondary data analysis.* Kings College, London.

McCormack B (2003) Supporting residents and relatives in Phair L, Benson S *Handbook for Care Assistants 6th edition.* Hawker Publications, London.

McIver S, Wyndham R (2013) *After the error. Speaking out about patient safety to save lives.* Toronto, Canada.

Miller D P, Swain A D (1987) Human error and human reliability in Ootim B (2002) Error making Part 2: Identifying the causes in nursing. *Nursing Management* 9, 1, 25-29.

NHS Commissioning Board (2013) *Compassion in Practice Nursing, Midwifery and Care Staff: Our Vison and Strategy*. Department of Health, London.

Panorama (2014) Behind Closed Doors: Elderly care exposed. www.bbc.co.uk.

Pearson A (2006) Powerful Caring. *Nursing Standard* 20, 48, 20-22.

Perry B (2009) Conveying compassion through attention to the essential ordinary. *Nursing Older People* 21, 6, 14-21.

Phair L, Benson S (2003) *Handbook for Care Assistants 6th edition*. Hawker Publications.

Phair L, Good V (1998) *Dementia a Positive Approach*. Whurr Publications, London.

Phair L, Heath H (2010) Neglect of older people in formal care settings part one: New perspectives on definition and the nursing contributions to multi-agency safeguarding work. *The Journal of Adult Protection* Vol. 12, 3, 5-13.

Phair L, Heath H (2010) Neglect of older people in formal care settings part two: New perspectives on investigation and factors determining whether neglect has taken place. *The Journal of Adult Protection* Vol. 12, 4, 6-15.

Phair L Manthorpe J (2011) Health care and adult safeguarding: an audit informing the relationship of the UK vetting and barring scheme with the NHS. *The Journal of Adult Protection* Vol. 13 NO. 5, pp. 251-258.

Schulz R, Herbert R, Dew M et al (2007) Patient suffering and care giver compassion: New opportunities for research, practice and policy. *The Gerontologist* 47, 1, 4-13.

Scottish Government (2009) *Adult Support and protection (Scotland) Act 2007*. Code of Practice Scottish government Edinburgh.

Smallbone S (2008) *Preventing child sexual abuse: Evidence Policy and Practice.* Wilken Publishing, London.

Van der Cingel M (2011) Compassion in Care; A qualitative study of older people with a chronic disease and nurses. *Nursing Ethics* 18 (5) 672-685.